*PSYCHOTHERAPY*

*IN*

*THE SOVIET UNION*

# Psychotherapy in The Soviet Union

*Translated and edited by*
**RALPH B. WINN, Ph.D.**

**PHILOSOPHICAL LIBRARY**
New York

*Printed in the United States of America*

# CONTENTS

Translator's Preface, by *Ralph B. Winn*     ix

## PART I

### THEORETICAL PROBLEMS OF PSYCHOTHERAPY

Certain Theoretical Questions of Psychotherapy,
by *V. N. Miassischev*     3

Speech Therapy, by *K. I. Platonov*     21

General Methodological Problems of Psychotherapy, by *M. S. Lebedinsky*     37

On the Neural Mechanism of Hypnosis, by
*I. I. Korotkin* and *M. M. Suslova*     40

Bio-Electrical Activity of the Brain in Hypnotherapy, by *M. P. Nevsky*     44

Effect of Conditioned Stimulation in the Waking
and Hypnotic State on Human Digestive
Secretion, by *Y. M. Levin*     52

Concerning the Physiological Foundations of
Psychotherapy, by *A. K. Troshin*     55

Basic Methodological Questions concerning
Group Psychotherapy in Neuroses, by
*N. V. Ivanov*     57

Methodology of Suggestion in the Waking State,
  by *I. S. Sumbayev*                                              61

PART II

## PSYCHOTHERAPY OF NEUROSES

Therapeutic Methodology in Psychasthenia, by
  *E. K. Yakovleva*                                                69
Psychotherapy in Phobic States,
  by *A. M. Haletsky*                                              73
Therapy of Certain Forms of Hysteria,
  by *Z. A. Kopil-Levina*                                          78
Combination of Psychotherapy with Medicinal
  Sleep, by *O. R. Chitava*                                        82
The Method of Indirect Suggestion as Used in
  Hysteria, by *Y. L. Schreiber*                                   85
On the Psychotherapy of Psychogenic
  Impotence, by *I. M. Apter*                                      89
Psychotherapy in the Medico-Pedagogic Practice
  of a Child Psychiatrist, by *N. G. Veshapelli*                   94
Psychotherapy of Child Stuttering,
  by *N. A. Vlassova*                                              98

PART III

## PSYCHOTHERAPY OF PSYCHOSES

The Role of Psychotherapy in the Treatment of
  Psychoses, by *N. V. Kantorovich*                                105
On the Psychotherapy of Schizophrenia,
  by *A. N. Molokhov*                                              113
The Use of Medication and Psychotherapy in
  Psychiatric Clinics, by *A. S. Poznansky, M. I.
  Zeitlin,* and *I. G. Tokareva*                                   117
The Record of Psychotherapeutic Work in
  Mental Hospitals, by *L. I. Lichtenstein*                        122

# PART IV

## TREATMENT OF ALCOHOLISM AND SMOKING

On the Role of Suggestion in the Treatment of
Alcoholism, by *I. L. Lukomsky*  129

Unique Factors in the Hypnotic Treatment of
Chronic Alcoholism, by *T. N. Gordova* and
*N. K. Kovalev*  136

A Study of Selective Rapport in Hypnosis, by
*I. O. Narbutovich*  141

Psychotherapy of Smoking, by *Y. A. Povorinsky*  144

# PART V

## PSYCHOTHERAPY IN SOMATIC AILMENTS

Use of Hypnotherapy in Cases of Bronchial
Asthma, by *I. I. Bull*  155

Psychotherapy in Psychogenic Thyreotoxicosis,
by *M. I. Kashpur*  161

The Significance of Psychotherapy in Obstetrics
and Gynecology, by *V. I. Zdravomyslov*  165

Psychotherapy of Hypogalactia of Nursing
Mothers, by *A. T. Belyaeva, G. I. Vinokurov,
V. I. Zdravomyslov, T. M. Kravchenko*, and
*N. I. Kuymova*  169

The Use of Hypnosis and Conditioned-Reflex
Therapy in Dermatology, by *M. M. Zheltakov*  172

Hypnotherapy of Dermatoses in Resort Treatment, by *I. A. Zhukov*  178

# PART VI

## GENERAL PROBLEMS

Psychotherapy of Convalescence, by
*I. P. Kutanin*  185

Psychotherapeutic Factors in Clinical Practice,
by *A. S. Borzunova, A. V. Sayfutdinova,
Z. M. Akhmetova, O. P. Klimovich,* and *A. I.
Sannikova*                                            190
Psychotherapy in Iatrogenic Illnesses, by *M. A.
Zhilinskaya* and *L. G. Pervov*                       195
Group Psychotherapy and the Movies, by
*L. M. Sukharebsky*                                   199
Index                                                 203

## Translator's Preface

The collection of papers that follows was read at the last conference on psychotherapy in the Soviet Union (Moscow, 1956). There is a marked shift of emphasis in research since the preceding conference of the same kind, held in 1948. I. P. Pavlov's influence remains, true enough, as strong as ever. But increasing attention is being paid now to the use of suggestion, hypnosis, and speech therapy in general; in fact, almost all papers contained in the book have something to say concerning these methods of treatment. Alcoholism is obviously on the increase and calls for a more vigorous and advanced study. Psychoanalysis, previously much criticized, receives hardly any mention at all.

On the whole, the differences between our own methodology of psychiatric treatment and what we find in the Soviet Union are so striking as to make one wonder whether there is any similarity in the theoretical and practical application of the two techniques. This can be explained in part by the fact that psychotherapy is, after all, but a part of psychiatry and largely excludes the treatment of psychoses and mental deficiency. But even so, it is somewhat surprising that we find many topics in the collection dealing with what is hardly discussed at all in the American psychiatric journals. Among the papers that ought to arouse much interest in our medical circles are "Psychotherapy of Smoking" (by Y. A. Povorinsky), "Use of Hypnotherapy in Cases of Bronchial Asthma" (by I. I. Bull), "The Significance of Psychotherapy in Obstetrics and Gynecology" (by V. I. Zdravomyslov) and "Group Psychotherapy and the Movies" (by L. M. Sukharebsky).

If this book is to be of value to the American readers, it must be approached in the spirit of scientific objectivity. It contains certain attitudes common to Russian scholars which we are often unwilling to share; but these attitudes are clearly customary among the Soviet writers. Nevertheless, whatever worthy contributions they have to offer must not be nullified by our antagonism. Truth is, in the end, truth on both sides of the iron curtain. And whatever falsity exists anywhere in the world will be found out sooner or later.

RALPH B. WINN

*Monmouth College, N. J.*

*PSYCHOTHERAPY*

*IN*

*THE SOVIET UNION*

PART I

*THEORETICAL PROBLEMS OF
PSYCHOTHERAPY*

# CERTAIN THEORETICAL QUESTIONS OF PSYCHOTHERAPY

## by V. N. Miassischev
### (*Leningrad*)

It is no longer necessary to demonstrate the value of psychotherapy. Its high prestige is merely a consequence of successful clinical experience and expresses the noble humanitarian traditions transmitted to us by outstanding representatives of our national medicine.

The experience of neurological, psychiatric, and other specialized clinics enables us to regard psychotherapy as an important method, or rather as a collection of methods, of treating not only mental and psychogenic illnesses, but also those of psychosomatic causation.

Psychotherapy derives its significance from the fact that the causative factor in the development of certain diseases is psychological in origin. That is why neuroses happen to form the most important area in the development and application of psychotherapy.

The principal and most urgent questions of psychotherapy in our day are: (1) the formulation of

3

theoretical principles in the field of psychotherapy; (2) clarification of effective conditions in the use of psychotherapeutic methods; and (3) discovery of reliable criteria for the choice of psychotherapeutic technique for each particular case.

The method of psychotherapy offers in the last analysis a way of influencing one human being (the patient or a group of patients) by another (the physician). As a result, the psychotherapeutic method turns out to be uniquely human, and its appreciation and mastery depend upon understanding of the personality traits of various individuals as social and biological creatures.

Man differs from animals in that he is capable of engaging in speech and abstract thinking relevant to the processes of work and social relations. Each man is not merely an object, but also a subject consciously reacting to conditions of his surroundings and, on occasion, intentionally transforming them.

The evolution and re-organization of psychotherapeutic theory is rooted directly in these psychological traits of human beings and, consequently, it is capable of throwing light upon various psychogenic ailments such as personality troubles; this theory emerges from insights into human personality and its modes of response to immediate reality in the form of experiences and activities.

The problems of psychogenesis as well as psychotherapy cannot be fully solved apart from materialistic psychology. The contemporary Soviet psychology has grown on the foundation of the general theory of dialectical and historical materialism as well as the physiological doctrines of I. P. Pavlov. It has been built

4

on the understanding of man in the light of scientific and social history.

While fighting the faults of idealistic psychology, we must also fight any one-sided approach to human nature which considers merely the mechanism of neural activity and thus disregards the underlying motivating forces.

Scholars and even rank workers in everyday medical practice are confronted with the job of developing the legacy of Pavlov; but this task does not consist merely in automatically repeating Pavlov's words, but rather in deepening and making more intelligible our conception of man, in all his activities, as a union of psychology and physiology.

It is quite clear by this time that all the critical remarks uttered by Pavlov with regard to the psychology of his day were directed above all against any exclusively psychological (or, for that matter, exclusively physiological) interpretation of experiments on animals, and also against any type of idealistic methodology.

I. P. Pavlov put the psycho-clinical approach to health and disease ahead of the physiological one. He repeatedly expressed the belief that the time has come for bringing physiology and psychology together and for clarifying the function of psychology in psychiatry. He stressed the need for every psychiatrist to be also a psychologist, at least in the empirical sense of the word.

In the meantime, scientific achievements in the physiology and pathophysiology of the higher neural activities supplied physicians with the knowledge of the laws of normal neural activity, complex interrelations among individual processes, and mechanisms of pathological deviation.

It was then that I. P. Pavlov brought forward his concept of the secondary signal system existing exclusively in man. "Words," he declared,* "can serve as real conditioning stimuli beyond any quantitative or qualitative comparison with any other stimulation in animal life." In other words, the symbols forming speech are unique in significance and, for human beings, they are subject to certain specific laws. Unfortunately, however, such laws have not yet been reduced to either normal or pathological physiology.

Though the union of psychology and physiology presents a definite research task and sets a desirable, even necessary, goal for scientific progress, neither psychology nor physiology, each by itself, has so far been able to solve the main problems of psychogenesis or psychotherapy. This becomes particularly obvious when we consider the prevailing views on personality, experience, and human relations.

By human relations we understand the process of forming selective ties with various aspects of one's environment; and by one's personality we mean a pattern of such selective attitudes. These concepts have been shown to be of great significance, from the Pavlovian standpoint, for gaining insight into mental as well as neural activities of man.

This view becomes even more significant when examined in the light of Marx-Lenin methodology in general, or more specifically in application to Soviet pedagogy, the most remarkable representative of

* I. P. Pavlov, *Clinical Environments* (in Russian), I, 415.

6

which is A. S. Makarenko. That is why we take this view as our starting point for all investigation of neuroses, psychogenesis, and psychotherapy.

The concept of human relations, which serves to synthesize man's manifold connections with objective reality, is derived from the concepts of reflex, reaction, and the underlying vital impulses, and also from the more complex processes of human neural activity. At the top of their development, human relations involve some exceedingly complex social products—such as beliefs—which are grounded in human speech and thought, and which represent the highest ideological level of conduct.

The concept of personality as a system of human attitudes applies to all levels of human relations, from mere incidental impulses to well-established convictions.

Another psychological element of considerable importance is that of emotion; it is so well known to physiologists that some of them regard it as fundamentally physiological. In this connection, some people assume that emotion is inseparable from the subcortical regions of the brain, that it is but a complex unconditioned reflex. This may be so, phylogenetically. But when it comes to emotions involving aesthetics and ethics, we have to meet the tasks of interpreting physiology of emotions at the contemporary historical and social level attained by man in his development. It is quite obvious, therefore, that the manifestation of human emotions is determined by the formation of a dynamic system of close but temporary ties between cortical and subcortical processes. The cortical excitations appearing in the so-called higher emotions involve specifically human components of neural activity, thus underlying and occasionally directing speech, thought and behavior of man, and establishing through stimulation close and firm, yet temporary, connections.

Intellectual interest, inspiration, or painful moral conflict do affect the entire human organism. These factors turn into a source of irresistible impulses, unforgettable experiences, and persistent impressions.

It is necessary to state clearly and emphatically that psychology on the whole disregards the fact that emotions are found in three distinct but otherwise closely connected variations. There are, first of all, acute emotional reactions with lasting effects; second, there are emotional states, during a mental illness, overwhelming the whole man and affecting all of his experiences; and third, there are changeable emotional attitudes which, in pathology, create prejudicial feelings or one-sided or excessive reactions. Pathological states, such as melancholia, and psychogenic developments, such as paranoia or delirium of jealousy, represent clinical forms of emotional manifestation inseparable from pathological changes.

In human beings as distinct from animals the role of traces of past experience is so great that reactions depend much less on the immediate stimulation than on the relevant experience in the past; indeed, the effect of stimulation depends mainly on one's attitude as determined by the past. This can be occasionally observed in animals, too, but in a much less generalized form than in man. Psychogenic disturbances are also connected with acute, overwhelming experiences which, in turn, can be accounted for only in terms of emotional relations. A mere fright or shock connected with these experiences represents reactions the mech-

8

anism of which is relatively independent; but in all other cases, both the pathological reaction and the pathological state are connected with emotionally saturated relations of unique significance to a person. To exemplify: unfaithfulness or death of the beloved, a personal insult, or a sharp internal conflict form the pathogenic situations becoming the more unbearable, the stronger have been the tensions developed in the course of one's life history. The loss of a dear friend becomes a hard blow only if one feels a strong emotion toward him, say, love. An insult produces a sharp reaction only if it creates some sort of break with the past. The mechanism of these shocks was well demonstrated by I. P. Pavlov in his experiments on animals. But the study of human psychogenesis must yet show how, in the long run, one's attitudes are formed to give rise to the extremely strong reactions we observe, which lead to breakdowns of neural activities and to pathological mental or somatic conditions.

In this connection, it is important to say a few words concerning the nature of neural activity. Here we shall mention only one highly important fact: that the typical characteristics of a person develop differently in different systems. Thus, a physically weak type may, depending on home upbringing or place of birth, become characterized by moral strength or stability or else combine intellectual mobility with depth of emotions.

From this we can draw the conclusion that it is insufficient to describe the first case merely as weak or strong and the second case as mobile or inert. All this does not change Pavlov's postulate that the outcome of any emotional strain depends basically on the correlation between the difficulty of the problem of

9

life and the individual's strength of nerves. But in the case of man at least, a further qualification is indicated as to where his typical traits are leading, in what he is weak and in what strong; in other words, the source of his pathology is to be sought not merely in the type of his personality as a whole, but also in the weaker links of his neural make-up.

In this connection, the question as to the source of pathology must always be properly investigated and evaluated. If we happen to be dealing with an experimental animal, the source lies probably in the disturbance connected with the solution of one of its major problems; if we deal with a human being, however, it is more likely to be a person or a group of persons, a circumstance or a combination of circumstances that becomes unbearable. In all this it is not so much the persons or circumstances themselves that count, but rather one's attitude toward them; and it is this attitude rather than anything else that raises one's sensitivity to the point of dangerous strain. Such attitudes are no mere manifestations of specific irritability; they have also a history that establishes, or prepares for, the source of pathology. A more or less simple annoying circumstance is here replaced by a more generalized meaning of the circumstance. Stimulation of this source of pathology may produce, as has been clearly shown on animals, a badly modified reaction, permitting us to speak of aspects of the source of pathology, complicated in more serious cases by the spreading of it to other neural systems.

If experimentation enables us to bring about the formation of pathogenic attitudes in animals, clinical studies permit us to account for the origin of some pathological states in man by means of the so-called subjective and objective anamnesis. The analysis of any given pathology, in clarifying the history of the case, helps us considerably to determine the purposes of treatment. But, in doing so, it is necessary first of all to consider two types of pathogenesis. In the first type, the originally wholesome personality forms pathological attitudes and may eventually result in a breakdown, if confronted with difficult conditions of life; in the other, not only the attitudes but also the character itself changes under the influence of continually unfavorable conditions, so that the very ground of behavior becomes pathologically altered. Actually, however, the distinction is usually but of theoretical value, for we find all kinds of combinations and modifications of the two types. In a therapeutic situation, we must concentrate largely on this complex background itself, without going into any further study.

It is necessary, moreover, to concede that both attitudes and the character as a whole are never completely fixed. Even though some attitudes and traits are fairly stable and consequently difficult to change, under concrete conditions of life, they prove to be dynamically flexible.

Nevertheless, it is exceedingly important to acknowledge that even the most difficult states, such as the inward and outward attitudes of conflict and all kinds of troublesome experience, can be cured or relieved by psychotherapy. It is well known to us that the foremost psychotherapeutic approach consists in influence of words. One wonders where the word gathers its massive resources required for the vital rehabilitation occurring in the sick person under the influence of psychotherapy. At the same time, we

11

must also concede that, while in many cases the medical use of words brings about excellent results, in other cases it remains completely helpless and futile.

Psychotherapy, as a process of social interaction between the physician and his patient, must not be regarded, however, as merely verbal. Consequently, it would be as wrong to identify psychotherapy with 'speech therapy' as to replace the concept of higher nervous activity by the narrower concept of speech, which is but the secondary signal system. Even in this sense, the meaningful, expressive and activating elements of psychotherapy consist not only of speech, but also in facial expressions and gestures, in utilizing endless associative connections saturated with imagery and emotional components.

The dry and pedantic utterances of a tired physician will not cure a single patient. But suggestions—disturbing, arousing, inspiring suggestions—represent a complex and dynamic system of words and meanings, imagery and motions, as well as a functionally psychological and, consequently, physiological totality capable of combining a dynamic form and a significant content.

There are two basic forms of psychotherapeutic influence—suggestion and persuasion; they differ mainly in the purpose of activating words. Sometimes they are contrasted as the irrational method and the rational one. In the first instance, the efficiency of the word is determined by changes in the response of the patient's cortical centers in the state of hypnosis. In the second instance, the cortical inhibitions and facilitations typical of hypnosis are absent; in fact, the process of persuasion is found among the highest activities of the secondary signal system and makes conscious and critical analysis readily accessible to the patient.

The question arises as to the susceptibility of the patient to hypnosis and his ability fully to assimilate the given suggestions. Two factors are usually mentioned in this connection: first, the qualities of his personality, such as suggestibility; and second, resistance arising in the disinclination to get well or even in the actual desire to stay sick. But the main and decisive element in either alternative is the patient's attitude toward his physician. Patients develop the feelings of respect, trust and affection toward the physician only gradually, insofar as he enables the patient, by a skilful approach to him, to comprehend in a sound perspective his life and particularly the complex, obscure and confusing circumstances of his past and present.

All this applies to hypnotherapy. It is well known among the professional people that there are two main forms of hypnosis. One is inseparable from an emotional attitude toward the hypnotist who becomes the source of overpowering stimulations comparable to strong sounds or bright lights. The other form of hypnosis has the opposite effect: it pacifies, makes one sleepy. In all this, the hypnotist and his words remain the only link between the patient and the outside world—indeed, the only directive force.

I. P. Pavlov used to contend that the nervous system represents virtually a self-regulating mechanism, the nearest to perfection. From the standpoint of clinical psychopathology, a typical neurosis as distinct from psychoses is characterized by a comparatively correct interpretation of the physical and social reality; but it conspicuously fails in self-control and self-possession.

And so in neurasthenia we observe disorganization of the ability to concentrate attention and to manage one's emotions; in obsession we cannot disregard the continual struggle within the patient's mind; and sufferers from hysteria live by impulses which control them rather than the other way around.

The psychotherapist is therefore the person whose support and encouragement is badly needed by the patient if the latter is to regain normal self-control. Unfortunately, however, the physiology of human regulation is not yet sufficiently known. We are informed, of course, that it plays some significant role in the secondary signal system and that, more specifically, it is often able to improve the mobility of various general mechanisms; but the job of deciphering all the major physiological details involved in the processes still remains to be done.

The role of the psychotherapist in the life of his patients becomes fairly clear as we observe a variety of patients coming to their doctor after they have lost much of the power over themselves and succumbed to the peculiar phenomena of their sickness, and especially after they have given up hope in a spontaneous recovery. Without exaggeration, it is right to declare that to an average patient the physician becomes a teacher of life. He must devote a great deal of attention to the re-education of the patient and try to do for him all he can.

Sometimes it is exceedingly difficult even for an experienced psychotherapist to determine the precise

14

cause of mental illness, and it is here that the patient can be of great and active service.

When the first attempt at diagnosis is being made and the sources of illness are being sought, the patient's sensitivity may be aroused at the approach to "touchy points"; but subsequently, as the pathogenic complex begins to unroll, the symptoms begin slowly and gradually to disappear.

The process of comprehending the pathogenesis of one's disease is at the same time a process of re-establishing associative connections which have become neglected and isolated as a result of various automatisms or compulsions. When the seat of these troubles is finally removed, the patient regains reasonable self-control over the relevant experiences.

E. K. Yakovleva and myself have described elsewhere a case of deep hysteria, in which the woman would walk into the woods where she would moan and groan for quite a while and, on her return home, she would grab an axe and swing it violently over her baby's head. During all this the woman was, strangely enough, perfectly aware of what she was doing. The question is: what was the cause of this queer behavior?

As a detailed study of the case has demonstrated, at the root of the patient's conduct lay wounded self-love. At her parents' home she had always been the center of attention. When she was married, her attitudes remained essentially the same, and she assumed the domineering attitude toward her husband and, later, her children. But during the Second World War the patient found herself alone for many months, in the conditions where she had to consider others and even obey them. When at the end of the hostilities she was reunited with her husband and children, she discovered that they had changed and wanted reasonable respect. This made her feel strangely lost, for she was utterly unable to make adequate concessions to the demands of reality. Then she began to fight bitterly and stubbornly in order to regain her domineering position in the family, but her cries expressed only rage and feelings of futility. Nevertheless, the patient fully recovered in the end when, with her physician's assistance, she was enabled fully to comprehend the cause of her illness and to reconstruct her everyday attitudes on a more realistic basis.

Another patient was suffering acutely from fear of death. True enough, she had an enlargement of the heart and suffered from tachycardia. But her mental state had little to do with this pathology. The actual cause of it could be established only after a careful study of her life history. It was then learned that the fear of death was actually the fear of insecurity and loss of self-respect.

It all began with a love affair in the course of which she contracted gonorrhea, of which she was shortly cured. When a few years later she was married to another man, she failed to tell him the truth, particularly concerning the venereal disease. For twenty years she lived with her husband perpetually worrying about her secret.

Analysis of this patient's past was clearly indicated in the case. She grew up in a peasant family in which sexual morality was strictly, unconditionally enforced. When she fell in love with the man infecting her with gonorrhea, she suffered deeply, but remained otherwise quite normal. Nevertheless, when she was eventually married to another man, she proved to be frigid. In the waking state she never experienced any sexual attraction or satisfaction; but she had from time to time erotic dreams indicating that her sexual impulses were merely inhibited. It was clear that with regard to the painful question of the broken trust and deception she felt herself as guilty as was the man involved in the affair before her marriage. Though the apparent cause of her illness was a sexual tragedy, actually it was a question of moral conflict and the danger of being found out. Both her fear of death and pain in the heart were but manifestations of her tormenting scruples and worries.

It is worth mentioning that the patient's complaints of heart disturbances increased after a later attack of angina; but neither of these troubles stood in the way of disappearance of her symptoms once the mental conflict was resolved. Having turned trustfully to her physician, she proceeded actively to cooperate in the clarification of her pathogenic problems. Soon afterwards she lost her anxieties completely and became normally calm and relaxed.

As an additional example, we take the case of a woman whose husband had been repeatedly unfaithful to her. As a result, she developed fear of cancer. The truth was that the patient regarded her husband's conduct as a shocking insult to herself, making it completely impossible for her to trust him any longer. This alone constituted the original cause of her mental condition.

All these examples of illness merely illustrate the great variety of moral frustrations and conflicts responsible for severe damage to mind and body.

17

The so-called "sexual trauma" represents in these cases but an outer appearance capable of assuming a great variety of forms, which only conceal entirely different and highly individual traits of personality.

Wherever illness arises suddenly and ends with the recovery of the affected function, there is no serious reason to expect its recurrence, unless it is complicated by pathological traits of character.

And finally a few things have to be said concerning the principle of choice in therapy. Here it is necessary to concede that different methods of treatment may lead to essentially identical results. In this connection, the choice of method must be left entirely to the physician.

Nevertheless, there are certain objective grounds for the choice. Acute psychogenic forms of neurosis are likely to call for hypnotic suggestion. In functional illnesses where the normal activity of the internal organs or skin is affected only as the result of strong nervous tensions, without any marked changes in the personality structure, hypnotic suggestion again brings the best and quickest results. But there are instances of "neuroses of organs" concealing much more complex psychogenesis, in which case deep psychotherapy is definitely indicated.

The patient's attitude of passive suffering toward his ailment makes hypnosis preferable in the initial stages of treatment, but it should be followed by narco-psychotherapy.

The method of distraction, too, plays an important role in psychotherapy. It has been used for a long time in the treatment of neuroses, and was specifically recommended by V. M. Bekhterev. It does not directly affect the pattern of the patient's attitudes, nor does

18

it conspicuously alter his character; but it does remove the patient's mind from the sources of painful experiences and, to that extent, is justified both psychologically and physiologically. In successfully distracting the patient's attention from the symptoms of his illness, the physician is able to revive his interest in life and thus enables him to form new associations of ideas. This method provides a ready physiological advantage in that it creates new centers of stimulation which act, by way of negative irradiation, to weaken the central mechanisms of the pathological condition.

The method of group therapy, whether used in a hospital ward or a collective, deserves considerably more attention. Group hypnosis has already been extensively employed in the struggle against alcoholism. But otherwise it is now used only by a few individual therapists.

The main fault of group psychotherapy, as interpreted by foreign specialists, consists in its dependence on the teachings of S. Freud. We have several other and much more acceptable variations of group therapy, namely (1) discussion with patients of the forms and origins of different psychogenic ailments; (2) discussion of specific cases; and (3) analysis of one significant case in the presence of other patients.

Group psychotherapy is not an alternative to individual treatment; the two are usually combined. But it helps to promote the physician's suggestions and to enhance the effect of individual treatment.

From all this follows that psychotherapy is formed around protective, activating, and corrective elements of treatment. As a link in the chain of therapy, it can be combined with physiotherapy and pharmacotherapy. But most closely is it connected with the therapy of work and education which normalize social relations and stimulate neuro-psychic activity.

The Soviet psychotherapy, built on the traditions of Marxism-Leninism, Pavlov's physiology, and materialistic psychology, has a truly scientific foundation; it is closely related to hygiene and prophylaxis. Under conditions of a socialist society, it has every chance of extensive growth and fruitful application to the protection and restoration of the workers' health.

# SPEECH THERAPY

by K. I. Platonov
*(Kharkov)*

In this report we shall not speak of psychotherapy in general, but only of those narrower problems which involve the use of speech therapy, that is, the immediate curative influence of the physician's words in his dealings with the patient. The direct medical objective of this method is the patient's mental activity while the physician's basic tool is his word. The word in its activity upon the secondary signal system of the cortex goes beyond it and has an effect also upon the primary signal system inseparably connected with it and thus reaches the subcortical regions of the autonomic centers and the seat of unconditioned reflexes, notably those of instincts and emotions. In this manner it becomes possible to produce perfectly real and objectively recorded therapeutic effects.

Speech therapy thus proves to be a scientifically sound system of therapeutic influences on all the branches of the patient's higher nervous activity and, indirectly, upon all the functions of his organism, in its mental and somatic aspects.

21

Numerous physiological studies indicate that the effect of words, depending on their content, is capable of bringing about all kinds of physiological and bio-chemical changes in the human organism. It is possible in this way deliberately to influence the functions of the autonomic nervous system, even when it concerns, for instance, a local inflammation of skin.

Apparently there is not an organ or tissue in the human body the condition of which cannot be modified in one manner or another by means of words; that is to say, by way of the cortex. Moreover, it appears to be possible to alter the functions of organs in several distinct ways—to stimulate, to inhibit, and to modify in some other fashion. It is well known that the impulses leaving the cortex are able, to use K. M. Bykov's phrase, "to cause events in the life of an organism which are truly extraordinary." Such "extraordinary events" can take place also through the influence of words upon the dynamics of the cortex.

One form of such intervention in the routine physiological activities, as they occur in the human organism, is the state of hypnosis which may take place in certain cases under the influence of a single brief word "Sleep!" As a result, there may arise, in addition to certain cortical inhibitions, also a whole shift among processes of the autonomic nervous system in the direction of vagotonia.

Something of the same sort can happen also as a result of certain emotions, naturally-formed or suggested, for they, too, are capable of causing considerable changes in the activities of the autonomic system.

Our investigations have shown that under the influence of suggested emotions, it is quite possible,

22

for instance, to alter an individual's gastric functions manifesting themselves in the chemistry of stomach secretions and even identifiable in an x-ray examination.

In these suggestions, negative emotions (fear, sorrow, etc.) tend to reduce the tonicity of the cortex, to lower functional manifestations of organs, and to decrease processes of assimilation. On the other hand, positive or sthenic emotions, such as joy or confidence, tend to raise the functional vigor of organs, to improve processes of assimilation, and at the same time to strengthen the operations of the cortex.

Most valuable are the experimental proofs showing that it is possible by means of words to establish or to remove certain effects of sensory stimulation upon the cortex cerebri. For instance, the verbal command "You will fall asleep the moment you hear the bang of a hammer on a sheet of roofing iron" may be instantaneously and fully obeyed, as demonstrated by changes in the rate of breathing, pulse, blood pressure, and other symptoms connected with the autonomic nervous system and corresponding to the state of normal sleep. It is possible, furthermore, also to produce, through a proper modification of the verbal command, a completely indifferent attitude toward the same sensory stimulation.

Practically the same can be done with regard to the activity of chemical substances. If a man is given the suggestion, for instance, that the considerable amount of ethyl alcohol he is about to consume is actually plain water, the effects of intoxication may not be observed at all. Comparable results may be produced also with many other pharmaceutical preparations.

This possibility to act upon the cortical and even subcortical processes by verbal means and thus to modify, sometimes in a most striking manner, one's attitude toward the external and internal stimuli is undeniably of great importance.

It has been repeatedly demonstrated in the laboratory of A. G. Ivanov-Smolensky that it is possible to establish conditioned reflexes of the heart, blood pressure, and the pupil of the eye by means of a command, not by a hypnotizing physician, but by the subject himself. This finding throws a most interesting light upon the physiological grounds of auto-suggestion.

At the foundation of all these facts lies the existence of representation in the cortex of various physiological and bio-chemical processes occurring in the human organism. This clearly indicates the possibility—nay, the reality—of a wide range of influence of verbal stimulations on various life processes in the human organism, many of which are quite important in the psychotherapeutic approach to patients.

Prior to the work of I. P. Pavlov, speech therapy was regarded as tenable only in some psychogenic neuroses. At that time we were ignorant, however, of what areas of the cerebrum it may affect or what physiological mechanisms are involved in the elimination of neurotic states. But now we know full well that at the bottom of any development of psychogenic ailments lies a functional disruption of the higher neural processes, together with the lowered tonus of the cortex—disruption of the vigor, mobility and balance of its activities. Such are the psychogenic neuroses, psychogenic dysfunctions of the internal organs (the so-called neuroses of organs), and psychogenic psychoses.

Insofar as verbal stimulations act upon the cortex, speech therapy must be regarded as a basic treatment for all psychogenic disturbances, though used in a variety of ways. Consequently, it has several purposes, namely

(1) To determine the actual causes leading to, and calling forth, functional disturbances of the higher nervous system.

(2) To remove the operation of the factors which functionally weaken the cortex, including various forms of negative emotions.

(3) To overcome or reduce serious functional disturbances of the higher nervous activities, among them disruption of any normal dynamic stereotypy.

(4) To create new and adequate cortical connections and thus to restore the patient's working ability.

(5) To enable the patient to get adjusted to the conditions of his external environment, thus preventing the likelihood of recurring disturbances in the future.

All this can be accomplished by means of:

(a) *persuasion* well grounded in facts and reasons, conducted during the patient's waking hours and assuming the form of calm assurances, encouragement, explanation, and clarification with active participation of the patient himself;

(b) strong verbal influence assuming the form of direct or indirect *suggestion* given in the waking state or sleep; and

(c) motivating suggestion conducted during an induced state of dozing or sleep, that is, *hypnosis*.

The methods of suggestion and hypnosis are today best understood and physiologically accounted for.

It is important to point out here that the use of speech therapy has greatly increased in the recent years, and it is now clearly indicated not only in psychogenic disturbances, but also in many other illnesses.

Particularly wide is its application in psychogenic neuroses with visceral breakdowns, such as breakdowns in metabolism, the gastro-intestinal tract, glands of internal secretion, breathing (as in bronchial asthma), the cardiovascular system (as in paroxysmal tachicardia). Essentially the same can be said of psychogenic disturbances of instinctive and emotional life, including the instinct of self-preservation, the maternal instinct, the sexual instinct as well as of emotional instability and various phobias.

Much attention is being paid nowadays to the precise identification of psychogenic dysfunctions connected with the malfunction of subcortical, endocrinal and visceral activities, insofar as diagnostic errors in these cases have been quite common lately, though readily discernible through speech therapy.

These errors are usually noticed whenever a physician fails to consider the possibility of psychogenic autonomic disturbances, particularly if the latter assume the semblance of organic faults (or "pseudo-organic syndromes," to use Dezherin's term). As a

26

result of this disregard, patients are often subjected to lengthy treatments, whereas speech therapy could have cured them without much delay.

Let us consider a few typical cases

(1) Patient K., a school principal, was suffering from intestinal malfunction once a month, on one and the same date. Various diagnoses were offered by different physicians. But eventually it turned out—when the coincidence of dates was noticed—that the actual cause of the ailment went back to a violent excitement produced by a fire in the school. Subsequently, the malfunction occurred regularly on the exact date of the fire as a result of the conditioned reflex. Three sessions of speech therapy, under conditions of suggested sleep, sufficed to remove every trace of pathology.

(2) Patient I., twenty-eight years of age, while working in the field, saw fire in her village and thought of her children. Frightened, she ran up the hill. On reaching the top, completely out of breath, she stopped and realized that the fire was quite a distance from her home. She fell, exhausted. But soon afterwards there appeared attacks of bronchial asthma and these recurred for five years. At that time, it became possible completely to remove the symptoms merely with six sessions of speech therapy. Catamnesis for three years was positive.

(3) Patient S., thirty years of age, began to develop conspicuous spots of baldness. A month-long dermatological treatment resulted in no improvement whatsoever. Then it became known that the loss of hair, in his case, began immediately after a tragic personal experience. Twelve sessions of suggestion

27

followed by sleep have completely restored normal hair growth. Positive catamnesis continued for about ten years; there was no recurrence of the symptom.

It is definitely established that speech therapy, particularly in its hypno-suggestive form, may be effective also in certain non-psychogenic, somatic diseases. It is particularly effective in various cases involving acute pains, especially in surgery without anesthesia, bad suffering in the post-operational period, difficult childbirth, anguish and agony in advanced cancer and tabetic crises. Good hypnotizability is important in these cases.

Speech therapy is also of considerable significance as an auxiliary symptomatic method of treatment in various somatic ailments. The problem here is how to raise the positive tonus of the cortex as well as the organism as a whole. Suggestion enables us in these cases to create calmness, relaxation, and stability in place of emotional states, to insure sleep, to improve the process of food assimilation, to restore appetite, and so forth.

Speech therapy has a well established role in the treatment of pulmonary tuberculosis. It has definitely a salutary effect upon sleep, appetite, and general well-being; in some instances it has been known to lower temperature.

Speech therapy can be of help also in removing excessively high sensitivity of the organism toward certain foods and drugs like quinine. This approach has been recommended by A. I. Kartamyshev, a dermatologist.

It follows from the preceding that speech therapy should be more widely used in every somatic clinic.

The usual ways of reassurance, encouragement, persuasion, and explanation, so commonly used in everyday medical practice, are, after all, among the essential elements of general psychotherapy. In this sense, every physician must be a psychotherapist.

In the treatment of neuroses, we employ the combination method of speech therapy. It consists in conducting an anamnestic talk with the patient or possibly even a number of such talks. It is easy in this way to clarify the concrete conditions and causes of the disease, to establish the desirable rapport with the patient, and to stimulate in him a trusting attitude toward the physician.

These anamnestic talks naturally lead to further steps of therapy, namely:

(a) waking speech therapy in the form of explanation, persuasion and encouragement;

(b) motivated suggestion in the hypnotic sleep, the purpose of which is to overcome whatever functional disturbances of the higher nervous system may remain;

(c) special verbal suggestion leading the patient to the state of deep rest, in which he remains for a definite prescribed time. We refer here emphatically to the state of deep rest because this kind of suggestion is capable of bringing about wider biochemical changes in the patient's organism than can possibly happen under the conditions of ordinary rest and tranquillity.

Let us now say a few words concerning the significance of speech therapy in the state of suggested sleep. At the foundation of this method lie two therapeutically valuable facts: first, that the inhibitions of sleep create the most favorable condition for the restoration of normal cortical activity disrupted by the disease; and second, that the functional specialization of the cortex makes possible both the direction and the specialization of the influence originating at the point of rapport, while the inhibitory action of sleep keeps the other portions of the brain steadily free, uninvolved. Moreover, every center of excitation so aroused becomes strengthened as a result of inhibition, according to the law of mutual irradiation. It is, consequently, particularly important to employ the correct forms of motivation for verbal influence, that is, the so-called "formulae of suggestion."

The use of hypnosis as a part of speech therapy is directly indicated in the cases requiring the strengthening of verbal effect, namely:

(a) Whenever at the foundation of a neurosis lies a psychic trauma characterized by an affectogenic lowering of the tonus of the cortex; for in these instances the state of suggested sleep is analogical or closely related to the state in which the pathological condition was originally formed in the cortical or subcortical area.

(b) In the reaction-type of neurosis the origin of which is known to the patient, even though he is unable to grapple with it by himself, whenever the disturbance does not yield to speech therapy in a waking state.

(c) Whenever it is necessary to help the patient in his attempts to make an adjustment to unfavorable but unavoidable external conditions, especially if the waking speech therapy is insufficient.

(d) In the presence of psychogenic situational

30

depressions occasionally accompanied by states of delirium or of endogenic and asthmatic depressions.

Among the most advantageous features of speech therapy using suggested sleep is the common and quite substantial reduction of the time required for treatment as compared to other and less widely successful methods, such as physiotherapy, pharmacotherapy, or change of conditions of life.

Our extensive observations of patients, extending back to ten or even twenty years, permit us to conclude that all the contentions to the effect that many results of hypnotherapy are impermanent are not exactly true. The simple fact is that much depends on the way it is administered.

Speech therapy with suggested sleep is likely to give excellent results in the reaction-type of neurosis of adolescents.

The evaluation of speech therapy, insofar as it employs hypnosis in the treatment of hysteria, must not disregard the widespread but erroneous belief that all it can achieve is to remove specific symptoms temporarily, for they are practically bound to be replaced by other symptoms. Our observations, the above contention to the contrary, permit us to conclude that the cure of hysteria may be complete and permanent.

However, we do not refer here to hysterical personalities of the weak and imaginative type where treatment must consist of a long series of measures aiming at re-education. Rather, we speak of individuals suffering from hysteria who are fundamentally healthy and strong but unable to face the conditions of unusually difficult life. In these cases, hysteria,

31

even if it be of long duration, proves to be but an episode in the patient's life. Our findings clearly show that mere duration of such neurotic ailments must not be taken for an obstacle to a quick and complete cure.

Essentially the same can be said with regard to the treatment of "obtrusive" neuroses, especially of phobias availing themselves of hysterical mechanisms and continuing for years. Positive results of treatment in such cases largely depend on combining speech therapy with some extensive and well-motivated formula of suggestion directed at the disclosure of causes of the ailment.

Let us next examine some of the pathological states in which the use of speech therapy with suggested sleep has been so far disregarded. We refer particularly to certain forms of epilepsy.

The question as to the place of psychic trauma in the development of the so-called "genuine" epilepsy is important though largely unexplored. The method of hypnotic suggestion is nevertheless indicated for some types of patients, especially when they are readily susceptible to it. We have indeed observed undeniable positive effects of speech therapy in those forms of epilepsy in which the preceding aura shows definite connection wih a psychic trauma. Hypnosuggestive therapy has been found advantageous also in the case characterized by worrisome expectation of regular seizures.

It may be interesting to point out that suitable combinations of speech therapy have been known to produce marked effects upon the patients suffering from psychogenic thyroidism, in its various forms

32

including Basedow's disease. The psychogenic form of this illness is quite common; yet, strangely enough, some patients find themselves on the surgical table, while others are sent to sanatoriums.

According to M. I. Kashpur, twenty-two out of seventy-five such patients of his had psychogenic etiology. Speech therapy had positive results within two or three weeks. In one serious case surgery became unnecessary. In the majority of the cases catamnesis continued for several years. A reduced basic metabolism, in addition to external signs of improvement, objectively demonstrated success of the treatment. These facts should be taken into consideration by the endocrinologists, surgeons and neuropathologists.

Good results of speech therapy with suggested sleep were generally observed in the toxicoses of pregnant women who as a rule do not react sufficiently well to pharmacotherapy. Out of 293 cases of pregnancy with toxicosis eighty-four percent ended in normal birth.

Studies conducted by M. Y. Miloslavsky (1951-54) at the Ukrainian Institute of Scientific Research for the Protection of Motherhood and Childhood (at Kharkov) show that, in cases of impending miscarriage, suggestions during hypnotic sleep have been able to reduce excitability of the uterus, to quiet down painful cramps, and to terminate bloody discharges. Of 387 such cases, eighty-seven percent resulted in normal birth.

The method of speech therapy either in the waking or sleeping state can be advantageously used also immediately after childbirth, notably in cases of malfunctioning mammary glands. V. I. Zdravomyslov has demonstrated the effectiveness of this method in disturbances of lactation.

In obstetrical practice, the method of conditioning by utilizing indirect suggestion may be of great benefit as a substitute for anesthesia. Research by I. T. Tsvetkov and K. V. Proniayeva on 223 observed cases has demonstrated that it is not inferior to any.

Quite interesting and highly significant are the observations of I. A. Zhukov, a dermatologist working at the warm springs at Sochi, which showed that speech therapy with prolonged sleep applied to 300 patients suffering from various dermatoses resulted in a highly increased percentage of cure.

Patients affected with eczema were, when so treated, cured three times as often as under the traditional types of treatment; those suffering from neurodermatitis recovered twice as often; and those afflicted with psoriasis, four times.

What are the essential conditions of success in speech therapy?

The main condition consists simply in a skilful approach on the part of the physician to his patient—his manners, his authority, knowledge and erudition in the field of speech therapy.

If this method in its elementary form of explanation, persuasion and calming is supposed to be at the disposal of every general practitioner, then a psychotherapist as a specialist, being also a psychiatrist and psychoneurologist, must feel at home in every physiologically-grounded method of psychotherapy used in a waking state as well as in suggested sleep.

What are the principal causes of failure in speech therapy?

Failure may sometimes occur as a result of wrong diagnosis; but more frequently it is a consequence of an insufficient contact between the patient and his physician, so that the latter does not take into consideration some relevant circumstances of the patient's life or experience, for instance, unfavorable social relations at home, at work, etc. Lack of success in the treatment of patients with weaknesses of the nervous system may sometimes be explained by the inability to create suitable conditions of life for oneself. Unsusceptibility to hypnosis may serve as another serious handicap to successful treatment. Occasionally the real difficulty lies in the patient's desire to pretend sickness, or to remain for some reason sick. Still another cause of therapy failure may be found in the physician's stubbornness to confine himself to a single method of therapy and thus to ignore other possibilities.

It must be acknowledged that the organization of speech therapy in hospitals often needs a considerable improvement. Now and then speech therapy assumes merely an incidental and haphazard form simply because many physicians have never been taught how properly to avail themselves of it. This indicates the dire need for putting short courses of training in practical psychotherapy at the disposal of general practitioners and also advanced courses to bring specialists up-to-date in their knowledge.

Moreover, the fundamental facts of psychotherapy and psychoprophylaxis should be known not only to physicians themselves, but also to the entire personnel working under them in various institutions.

If we are to improve public service in general, it is essential for us to extend the network of psychoneurological clinics. It is particularly important to make it possible for many patients to avail themselves of speech therapy without interrupting their work and normal conditions of life.

In addition, special psychotherapeutic offices should be organized in every psychiatric clinic, as they were once organized in the clinics of V. M. Bekhterev and S. S. Korsakov.

Psychotherapy must take from now on a prominent place in the field of medical practice.

# GENERAL METHODOLOGICAL PROBLEMS
## OF PSYCHOTHERAPY

by M. S. Lebedinsky
*(Moscow)*

The questions of psychotherapeutic methods are inseparable from their theoretical foundations and aims. But they could be established in the first place only after the study of the higher nervous activity was sufficiently advanced. The main task of psychotherapy is favorably to influence the patient's psychology by itself or in combination with other medical methods; to regulate the disturbed dynamics of the neural processes in his brain and thereby to restore the balance of functions in the whole organism.

As a branch of medicine, psychotherapy has at its disposal specific methods of its own. But in its broadest meaning it properly applies to the entire area of medical practice, no matter what the field of one's specialization may be.

Any accidental or purposeless effect of the physician upon the patient's psychology is likely to be insignificant and, moreover, harmful rather than beneficial. Consequently, it is very important to promote

37

the sound knowledge of scientific facts and psychotherapeutic methodology in the entire profession of
medicine. Each practising physician should know
how to exert psychotherapeutic influence upon his
patients, not so much during special sessions in his
office as in everyday contacts with them, that is,
during medical examination, daily rounds, while giving prescriptions, etc.

Psychotherapy can be used directly or indirectly,
through the entire organization of medical service
including the very environment in which the patient
lives.

One of the main purposes of psychotherapy is to
mobilize the patient's own activities so as to attain
the aims set by the physician in the course of
psychotherapy.

The main condition of any successful psychotherapy is that the patient have complete trust in the
physician and in the effectiveness of his method of
treatment. It is the first task of the physician, therefore, to decide how to promote the attitude of trust
in every one of his patients. To be able to do so, he
must carefully study the patient himself, his ailment
as well as the neurotic reactions that may have arisen
as a result.

The story of the personal experiences as related
by the patient to his physician is often quite frank
and full of details habitually withheld from other
people; but the telling of it is likely to decrease his
tenseness and improve his mental and physical condition. In offering intimate information concerning
himself, the patient simultaneously gets to know his
physician. It is quite important, consequently, that
the patient become thoroughly convinced of the

willingness on the part of the physician to listen attentively, to appreciate his plight, and to do everything possible for him. This close contact between the two and the resulting attitude of trust tend to make the patient somewhat calmer, less worried, and even stronger. His entire nervous system is thus favorably affected.

Our interpretation of the role of the physician in the patient's experience completely excludes the Freudian conception of the unconscious and the methods of catharsis and narcoanalysis.

# ON THE NEURAL MECHANISM OF HYPNOSIS

by I. I. Korotkin and M. M. Suslova
*(Leningrad)*

The problem as to how the neural impulses connected with hypnotic suggestion are spreading is, in our opinion, of considerable significance. Particularly interesting in this respect are the suggestions leading to the inhibition of certain responses.

It has been demonstrated by us that hypnotic suggestion in the absence of any conditioned or unconditioned stimuli results in the inhibition of these responses. It has been also shown that this inhibition avails itself of the mechanism of temporary neural connections. The stimulation "excluded" by this suggestion acquires the qualities of a conditioned inhibition.

A number of relevant facts permit us to ask this question: Do the stimuli retain their inhibitory effect in other applications than originally suggested?

To clarify this question we conducted observations on four patients suffering from hysteria, three of whom manifested somnambulism.

All of these patients were conditioned to show

defense reflexes with regard to several different stimuli. These conditioned reflexes included one to the sound of a metronome having 120 beats per minute (M), one to an electrical bell (E), and one to a buzzer (B). The specific reflex was blinking in response to M, and the closing of the eyes in response to E or B. A blast of air applied thrice to the inner corner of the left eye served as an unconditioned stimulation. After the patients' reflexes were examined, they were brought into the state of hypnosis. Certain specific suggestions were given them in that state. The effect of these suggestions was judged by the appearance of change in the reflexes taking place under hypnosis as well as in the posthypnotic state.

To get a convincing answer to the above question several experimental variations were devised in our study. We shall comment upon a few of these variations.

It was suggested to a patient a little before the experiment that the blast of air in the direction of the eye would be rather weak following the sound of the electric bell (E), but much stronger in connection with M. But actually the intensity of the blast did not vary at all. Prior to the suggestion, the responses were quite clear and equally strong whether they were preceded by the sound of the bell or that of the metronome. But subsequent to the suggestion the response became markedly different; the patient claimed that the stream of air following the sound of the bell was weak, whereas that following the sound of the metronome was strong, and correspondingly the reflex became weaker in one case and stronger in the other.

Then an additional suggestion was given: "There

will be no sound of either E or M." Actually, the conditioned stimuli were present just as before, but they had no direct effect whatsoever. In the post-hypnotic comments, the patient mentioned the absence of stimulation. It would seem, therefore, that the unconditioned stimulus, being invariably of one and the same strength would produce identical responses both with regard to E or M, neither of which was "heard." Nevertheless, the conditioned reflex was strong following the beating of the metronome and weak following the sound of the bell. The previous verbal comments continued, and the patient said in response to the unheard metronome that the blast was strong, and in response to the bell that the blast was weak.

So it seems that the conditioned responses, following the preceding suggestion, continued to be differentiated, even though the stimuli were no longer heard.

The second variation consisted in this that, instead of suggesting a different intensity of the blast of air following the application of different conditioned stimuli, it was suggested to the patient that there would be no blast of air directed into the eye following the sound of the buzzer (B). As a result, the response continued as before when the bell was ringing, but it became inhibited in the case of B, though the stimulus was actually applied.

Next, a new suggestion was given to the patient: "Both E and B will be discontinued from now on." Immediately after this the patient was aroused from hypnosis, and observations were continued in the posthypnotic state. The conditioned reflexes with regard to both stimuli, having been inhibited by the

42

suggestion, completely disappeared. Yet the unconditioned reflex manifested itself only after the sound of E. It would seem that the unconditioned response would be well expressed in both cases, insofar as the blast of air was applied in both instances, even though neither the bell nor the buzzer was heard. Nevertheless, in spite of the absence of any reaction to either E or B, the reflex was inhibited only with regard to the latter.

This variation indicates that, in spite of the fact that the "excluded" conditioned stimuli inhibit the corresponding conditioned reflexes, they continue at the same time correctly to react, in one case to the presence of the stimulus and, in the other, to the absence of the stimulus.

These findings throw an interesting light upon the mechanism of various activities familiar to the hypnotists, as when the subjects in a hypnotic state go around objects instead of bumping into them, even though their absence has been explicitly suggested.

Could it be that the same physiological mechanism accounts for the fact familiar to every psychotherapist that certain symptoms of disease become inhibited when so suggested, while others remain unaffected? Could it be that in the technique of suggestion we sometimes do not take sufficiently into consideration the multiform activities of pathogenic stimuli?

It may be proper also to conclude in general that extreme caution is indicated in influencing patients with words which are, after all, broad and complex sources of stimulation.

# BIO-ELECTRICAL ACTIVITY OF THE
# BRAIN IN HYPNOTHERAPY

## by M. P. Nevsky
### (Chelyabinsk)

Publications on the study of bio-electrical activity
of the human brain in the state of hypnosis remain
as yet relatively few.

In our own national literature, the first brief mention of change in this connection in the action currents
of the brain is found in the work of S. N. Subbotnik
and P. I. Spielberg (1949), who pointed out that,
during hypnotic sleep, the alpha rhythm is gradually
replaced by a slower one. Unfortunately, however,
the authors failed to make any comments upon the
health or sickness of their subjects. The next work on
record, that by A. I. Marenina (1952), was devoted
to the encephalographic study of hypnotic sleep. It
was conducted on mental patients in a clinic and
showed that the electric potential of the brain was
lowered in the state of hypnosis.

In 1954, I have arrived at the conclusion that
there are four bio-electrical stages arising successively
as a healthy person goes deeper and deeper into

hypnotic sleep. These changing conditions can be described as the stage of rhythm equalization, the stage of alpha spindles, the stage of minimal electric activity, and the stage of beta oscillations.

These data permit us to conclude that the hypnotic sleep of a normal person is characterized by a gradual decrease of electric activity in the brain (according to four stages) which, in itself, depends on the depth of hypnotic sleep.

In 1955, a symposium was published on the electric activity of the human brain in the state of hypnosis. The contributors were B. V. Pavlov, Y. A. Povorinsky and V. V. Bobkov, P. I. Spielberg, and A. I. Marenina. These authors confirmed the observation that, under hypnosis, the electric activity of the brain is lowered in proportion to the depth of the state.

In various papers by twelve foreign authors, seven (Loomis, Harvey and Hobart, 1937; Thompson, Forbes and Bowles, 1937; Lundholm and Loewenbach, 1944; Sirna, 1945; Dennes, 1947; Ford and Inger, 1948; Barker and Bergwin, 1948 and 1949) contended that hypnosis does not alter the electric activity of the brain and that inhibition does not lie at the foundation of the process. These authors concluded from this that hypnosis cannot be regarded as a state of sleep, insofar as sleep changes conspicuously the action currents of the brain.

The authors of five other works detected changes in the electric potential of the brain under hypnosis, but their findings contradicted one another. Some of them maintained (Frank, 1938; Frank and Koopman, 1938) that the electric activity of the brain characteristically rises under hypnosis; others (Blake and

45

Gerard, 1937) found that it falls; and still others (Marinesco, Sager and Crendley, 1937) noted that the alpha rhythm rises at first but slows down later, or else (Frank and Train, 1949) that it becomes "desynchronized" with the appearance of slow waves.

My own findings are the result of a study involving twenty patients with various neuroses (neurasthenia, psychasthenia, and hysteria). The records of bio-currents of the brain were taken under usual electro-encephalographic conditions by means of a double-channel cathode oscillograph. Hypnosis was induced through verbal fixation. The recordings of electrical activity of the brain were done before, during and after each hypno-therapeutic session, and also at the conclusion of the whole series.

Before I describe the dynamics of bio-electric activity of the brain (exclusively among neurotics) with pathological functions of the cortex, it is necessary to stress the peculiarities of electric activity of the brain under hypnosis in normal people, this serving as a norm for the estimate of any pathological deviations.

The regular modulated alpha rhythm was marked on each encephalogram taken before hypnosis; the same was done also with the normal (in frequency and intensity) beta rhythm. In the state of initial hypnotic drowsiness following the closing of the eyes (the first stage), the encephalogram showed leveling of the alpha rhythm, the lower amplitudes of the alpha waves going up while the higher ones become slightly flattened or hardly changed at all. These early fluctuations in electric activity of the brain under hypnosis constitute, in our terminology, the stage of rhythm equalization.

46

As the patient sinks deeper into hypnotic sleep more marked changes take place in electric activity of the brain, namely those characteristic of the stage of alpha spindles. Alpha and beta activities seem now to be pressed down, alpha waves proceed in groups of spindles, frequent and high at first and rare and low later on. The spindles of alpha waves continue for one-half to one and one-half seconds and alternate with periods of retarded rhythm. During all this time the subject is unable to open his eyes or to make any voluntary movement. This phase consists in the paralysis of voluntary activities if they are suggested. The decay and disappearance of alpha spindles with weakened beta rhythm indicates the transition of hypnotic sleep into a deeper form.

During this period it is quite possible to bring about somnambulistic experiences by means of verbal suggestion; they may be accompanied by either positive or negative hallucinations. This period does not as a rule result in amnesia.

As the depth of hypnosis is increased still further, electric activity of the brain goes down even more, the alpha rhythm disappears, the beta rhythm weakens, and the curve of bio-currents of the brain is clearly flattened. The brain enters now the stage of minimal electric activity.

The disappearance of both alpha and beta rhythms —they form the electroencephalogram of the normal waking state—is accompanied with the appearance of slow beta waves. The suggested somnambulistic experiences of the patient brought about during the minimal electric activity of the brain result as a rule in amnesia, complete or partial. It is important to note here that verbal suggestions and direct stimulations call forth the return and strengthening of the alpha rhythm in this period of hypnotic sleep. When the suggestions and the somnambulistic experiences connected with them are removed, one can observe within minutes or even seconds that electric activity of the brain, as shown upon the electroencephalogram, resumes its steady downward trend.

As soon as the subject is taken out of the hypnotic state by means of verbal suggestions, the waves promptly disappear from the electroencephalogram and are replaced by the alpha rhythm and beta rhythm, just as before hypnosis.

All this confirms the important fact that verbal suggestion in hypnosis and the hypnotic sleep as such leads to complex electro-physiological and bio-chemical changes in the cortex.

As to the effectiveness of hypnotherapy, our patients can be divided in three groups. Group A (ten persons) consisted of patients who recovered fully, with all the symptoms of illness gone. Group B (six persons) was composed of those whose condition improved, with some of the symptoms gone. To Group C (four persons) belonged those in whom no serious improvement could be observed.

The following changes in bio-electric activity of the brain were observed in Group A:

1. The well-expressed alpha rhythm was seen during the hypnotherapeutic sessions to go down, together with the weakening of beta-waves or, in a few cases, with their strengthening; occasionally the low alpha rhythm was accompanied by the appearance of slow beta-waves. Several patients revealed a brief stimulation of the alpha rhythm at the begin-

ning of hypnotherapy. These changes must be considered on the whole as favorable signs with regard to the effectiveness of hypnotherapy, insofar as they indicate the light and dynamic character of functional disturbances of the cerebral cortex. Indeed, the closer the character of bio-electric changes in the hypnotic state of the neurotics to the picture of the corresponding state in normal people, the better is the prognosis and the greater is the chance of quick recovery.

2. After a few (three to five) sessions of hypnotherapy, there were observed (immediately after the awakening from the state) certain changes on the electroencephalograms, characterized by the transition from a weakened and irregular alpha rhythm to a normal well-modulated alpha rhythm; the slow waves typical of the prehypnotic condition disappeared.

3. At the conclusion of the hypnotherapeutic sessions rather well-expressed alpha and beta rhythms were noticed in the electroencephalograms of the recovered patients (in six out of ten cases). Two patients showed a weakened and somewhat irregular alpha rhythm, while two others demonstrated moderate tachycardia with occasional alpha-waves.

Let us cite a couple of cases:

Patient P., thirty-six years of age, three years earlier had happened to work in the same office with another woman who suffered, it was learned, from tuberculosis of the lungs. As a result, she developed intense fear of contracting the disease. She realized that the chance of this was small, but she could not control herself, and the idea persisted. In the end, she could no longer overcome the irresistible desire to wash her hands repeatedly; then she began to wash the floors, doors, walls, tables in her apartment—practically everything.

It was then that she asked for medical help. Before the first session of hypnosis, encephalography of the right hemisphere of the cerebrum presented the picture of depression. The alpha rhythm was low and irregular; the beta rhythm was slightly accelerated. During the session, the picture changed considerably and remained fairly normal at its conclusion. But two days later, another encephalogram showed hardly any improvement. After five sessions of hypnotic treatment things began to look better. The patient was discharged after fifteen sessions. Catamnesis for two years confirmed her complete recovery.

Patient F., thirty-two years of age, suffered for about five years from erythrophobia. The electrical activity of her brain was characterized by a low though regular alpha rhythm and a weakened beta rhythm. At the conclusion of the hypnotic series the encephalogram revealed a definite improvement in the alpha rhythm and a perfectly normal beta rhythm. The patient recovered after sixteen sessions of hypnotherapy.

Among the patients in the Group B few changes were noticed in the electrical activity of the brain during hypnotherapy. Tachyarhythmia temporarily disappeared, but there was also some weakening of the alpha rhythm; slow beta-waves of short duration were observed at times.

The patients of the Group C manifested an inert, stable curve of electrical activity of the brain. Prior to psychotherapy, the encephalograms showed no alpha rhythm, but some tachyarhythmia, sometimes combined with theta and delta waves.

CONCLUSIONS:

1. The dynamics of bio-electrical activity of the brain in the hypnotherapy of neuroses is characterized by: (a) decrease of electrical activity of *the* brain during hypnotic sessions, with an occasional activization of the alpha rhythm or slow theta-waves; and (b) increase of the alpha and beta rhythms, with the normalization of electrical activity of the brain on completion of each hypnotherapeutic session.

2. The degree and type of changes in bio-electrical activity of the brain, as caused by hypnotherapy, have significant bearing upon the clinical interpretation of the state of the patient's sickness.

3. Small changes in electrical activity of the brain during hypnosis testify to the gravity of the neurotic condition.

4. The closer the changes in bio-electrical activities of the patient's brain during hypnotherapy to those observed in normal people under hypnosis, the better is the prognosis.

# EFFECT OF CONDITIONED STIMULATION IN THE WAKING AND HYPNOTIC STATE ON HUMAN DIGESTIVE SECRETION

by Y. M. Levin
*(Novosibirsk)*

The present paper constitutes a part of a larger research undertaking by a number of authors, namely, V. G. Fuchs, V. N. Panurova, Y. M. Levin, T. P. Maximova, Y. V. Natochin, Z. G. Androsova, and headed by S. S. Yudin.

For quite a while, the problem of the psychological aspect of stomach secretion has been arousing considerable interest. Hornborng, for instance, conducted extensive studies on a four-year-old boy with a fistula of the stomach. He demonstrated the existence of qualitative and quantitative differences in secretion during pretended feeding (under hypnosis) with meat, bread, and milk. I. N. Sheftel (1929) and I. N. Rybushkin and I. V. Danilov (1937) studied stomach secretions among patients with fistula. They confirmed the existence of the reflex aspect of secretion and affirmed the role of psychological factors during the initial stages of digestion.

52

Most noteworthy are the observations on gastric secretion stimulated merely by the hypnotic suggestion of eating, as demonstrated by V. I. Zdravomyslov. The resulting secretory effect closely corresponded to what happens normally in consuming, say, an ordinary breakfast. All these data, together with some additional new facts, were brought together in an article by S. S. Yudin (1940) entitled "Direct Verification of the Doctrine of I. P. Pavlov concerning Digestion."

Quite interesting also is the study of the actual relationship between the cortex of the brain and the internal organs it innervates, and of the respective roles of the sympathetic, parasympathetic, and humoral systems. In this connection, the plan worked out by S. S. Yudin is well worth examining. He proposed, namely, to study surgical patients with fistulae of the stomach, at various stages of the construction of an artificial oesophagus. To verify the exact paths of reflex impulses going from the cortex to the gastric glands, S. S. Yudin analyzed stomach secretion at various stages of digestion. In addition to regular meals, he used also meals which were merely suggested. In both kinds of "feeding," the curves of secretion were approximately alike. This was demonstrated by means of a special rubber sound introduced into the patient's stomach without causing any serious discomfort. Samples of secretion were taken every fifteen minutes and carefully analyzed both quantitatively and qualitatively.

These studies were conducted in a separate room under conditions of maximum silence. The patients were placed comfortably in beds. Some of the observations were made under hypnosis, others in the waking state. The fistula opening of the stomach was invari-

53

ably hidden from the patient's eyes by a special device permitting one to introduce food into his stomach—or to pretend doing it—without attracting his attention.

Working with a different group of patients, but under identical conditions, the experimenter combined the feeding with emotionally indifferent stimulations by sound. Four feedings sufficed to establish a conditioned reflex, each one preceded by remarks like, "When you hear the sound of a metronome, food will be introduced into your stomach," or "At the sound of a bell, food will be introduced into your stomach."

Once the conditioning was established, S. S. Yudin passed to the next stage of the operation in the construction of an artificial oesophagus, during which he performed a supracardiac vagotomy.

These studies demonstrate that it is quite possible, even after vagotomy, to obtain the rise of gastric secretion whether in the natural or hypnotic state. This seems to show that the pneumogastric nerves are not the only channel along which the impulses can be conducted from the brain and produce the reflex phase of gastric secretion.

# CONCERNING THE PHYSIOLOGICAL
# FOUNDATIONS OF PSYCHOTHERAPY

by A. K. Troshin
*(Sverdlovsk)*

Two of us, S. I. Serov and myself, have been studying various stages of hypnotic suggestion by means of the plethysmographic method. The plethysmographic curve undergoes changes in proportion to the depth of hypnotic sleep. More specifically, in a light sleep the waves of the plethysmogram sharply rise, but with the increasing depth of the state the picture becomes calm and fairly level.

The objective record of the functional state of muscles during hypnotic sleep is quite interesting. Electromyograms of the arm follow, even in their specific details, the amounts of the suggested static load. The suggested work—moderate, medium or hard—corresponds to what electromyograms indicate, thus objectively confirming the quantity of muscular work done during suggestion or hypnosis (A. K. Troshin and G. A. Shminke).

These data agree on the whole with the information available to us concerning the influence of the cortex and particularly of the secondary signal system on the activity of the lower centers of the brain.

The role of the cortex in the experience of pain is now well known. The following study on the effect of words upon pain was undertaken according to the method of motor sensography developed by A. K. Singaylo.

We first investigated the possibility of producing analgesia by means of spoken words as well as hypnotic suggestion. Then we examined changes in the thresholds of tactile and pain stimulation, and in the thresholds of endurance to pain; changes in the cortical inhibitions and in the defensive reactions to pain. In one series of experiments we studied these changes only after an explanatory talk on the safety of such stimulations and on the possibility of enduring them calmly. In the second series of experiments analgesia was suggested under hypnosis. The analysis of the results of the first series showed that in thirty-one out of thirty-four cases a simple explanation sufficed to raise the threshold of pain sensitivity and to increase the power of enduring it.

In the study conducted with M. P. Malkova on twenty patients we were able to demonstrate that it is possible to increase the number of leucocytes in the blood. After impressing positive emotions upon the subjects' minds (three to five minutes of suggestion), we were able to see that the number of leucocytes increased by 1200-1500; whereas after suggesting negative emotions their number decreased by 1300-1600. In a few instances, positive emotions resulted in paradoxical reactions.

# BASIC METHODOLOGICAL QUESTIONS
## CONCERNING GROUP THERAPY IN NEUROSIS

### by N. V. Ivanov
### *(Gorki)*

The physician's psychotherapeutic work calls for the promotion of wholesome types of activity in the patient, if the latter is to overcome his neurotic condition. This can be done in one of two ways: either by strengthening his protective inhibitions or by enabling him to form new centers of interest.

The method of group psychotherapy, as we use it, consists of talks conducted with patients twice or three times a week. During these talks the physician explains in a popular language what we know about neuroses and illustrates the more important facts with case histories of his former patients. He tries to convey to them the basic information concerning the etiology and pathogenesis of neuroses, to analyze in detail the conditions preventing possible recovery, and to show what practical measures are likely to be helpful in removing neurotic symptoms.

The starting point of this kind of treatment lies in getting thoroughly acquainted with each individual patient, learning about the circumstances of his life and the reasons for the fixation of the neurotic symptoms. As a result of this preparatory work, the patient usually assumes a positive attitude toward group meetings with the physician.

The purpose, from the physician's point of view, of the first talks with a group of patients is to overcome their unsound interpretation of their own illness, insofar as it creates the mood of depression and prevents the mobilization of available defense mechanisms. Accordingly, the physician tries to divert their attention to other things, above all to early signs of recovery. To achieve this, he devotes a couple of talks to details of treatment and patterns of better mental health.

These patterns include: (a) a gradual alleviation of symptoms of the disease; (b) a wave-like succession of health improvements and deteriorations in the patient's condition on the background of a slow restoration of normal attitudes; (c) a favorable turn in general condition with the weakening of, and occasional change in, symptoms; (d) disappearance of the manifestations of sickness in the presence of positive emotional experiences; and (e) the appearance of periods characterized by strong attempts to act contrary to the habitual fears and worries.

These preliminary talks have usually a good effect upon the patients. They become somewhat more observant with regard to signs of improvement and quite willing or even eager to discuss them with the physician.

The next step in this course of group psychotherapy consists in a detailed open discussion with

58

each patient of the conditions of his life, unfortunate influences, traumatic episodes. Some time is devoted also to a critical examination of various unhappy situations or events of the past and to possible conscious changes of attitude toward the sources of original trauma. This is done by offering an analysis of typical occasions for the formation of neurotic symptoms and pointing out that most of them arise as a result of overstraining the nervous system. These talks arouse a great deal of interest among the patients and thus make the subsequent individual work with them much easier.

At this stage of group therapy, most patients are anxious to have more contacts with the physician and are quite willing to tell him of specific happenings in their life. The success of this form of psychotherapy depends to a certain degree on the physician's prestige as well as on his attentive interest in each patient. It is important for the physician also to touch upon the questions connected with various "difficulties" of life and to deal factually with the experiences of all the participants. By this time he is regarded by the patients as a human being who had an opportunity to glance into their inner world. This impression goes a long way to overcome the belief so common among the neurotics that their predicament and sufferings are unique, something that no one else has ever experienced. It is only natural that the physician, even without asking any questions, is able to "guess" what is worrying his patients.

The crucial point at this stage of psychotherapy consists in this: that it provides an excellent opportunity for heart-to-heart relations with the patients.

Emotional reconstruction is often readily observed at this time. It is the job of the physician to encourage and strengthen the process.

During the third and final stage of psychotherapy the physician should insist on the active participation of all patients in the constructive group work, thus diverting their attention from the previous mode of living, that is, from their neurotic behavior. The general direction of the physician's comments at this time points toward the unconditional importance of the patient's return to employment as the best possible remedy.

The less the patient thinks of himself and his feelings, the more successful becomes the treatment. The last talk completing the course of group therapy is devoted to the prevention of possible disappointment among the patients that the talks are ending while they still have some signs of pathology.

Long experience in the use of the method described above has convinced us that group therapy has many advantages over individual treatment. For one thing, it permits an immense increase in the extent of medical service. It offers excellent opportunities for the physician to establish good contacts with his patients within a short period of time, thereby raising the chances of favorable developments. Explanatory talks conducted by the physician prove to be very convincing and are appreciated by the patients as providing serious scientific information rather than just routine consolation.

In short, group psychotherapy makes it incomparably easier for the physician to put at the disposal of his patients various ways and means of counteracting and alleviating their own symptoms.

# METHODOLOGY OF SUGGESTION IN THE WAKING STATE

by I. S. Sumbayev

*(Irkutsk)*

Suggestion and auto-suggestion can be achieved, as is well known, without resorting to hypnosis, that is, in the waking state. The methodology of hypnosis and of suggestion during it has already been thoroughly investigated; but the methodology of suggestion in the waking state has never before been seriously studied. And yet there is no longer any doubt that it can be of considerable help in extending the benefits of psychotherapy.

Some of the early scholars in the field (A. A. Liébault, H. Bernheim, A. A. Tokarevsky, V. M. Bekhterev, A. Forel, etc.) were able to show that particularly responsive individuals, under the influence of waking suggestion, can successfully demonstrate a number of interesting phenomena, such as catalepsy, automatic movements, anesthesia, hallucinations, etc.—which often arise under hypnosis. It was also observed that exceptional sensitivity to waking

61

suggestion is found mainly in individuals previously subjected to hypnosis.

As to auto-suggestion, it has been long known that it occurs as a rule in the waking state, particularly among those suffering from hysteria, where it is responsible for a great variety of neuro-psychic deviations so typical of the disease.

In the construction of the methodology of waking suggestion, it is desirable to keep in mind that hypnosis, as suggested sleep, is but one of several possible techniques of suggestion, since it can also assume the form of suggested intoxication, suggested ecstasy, suggested depression, etc.

Waking suggestion should fulfill, in our opinion, two essential conditions, namely:

(1) that it should not result in hypnotic sleep; and
(2) that it be capable of effecting essentially the same phenomena which are commonly observed under hypnosis.

After considerable planning and experimentation, we have arrived at the following rules and procedures adequately meeting the scientific purposes of waking suggestion.

It is always conducted in an ordinary physician's office in the daytime and without any special precautions with regard to lighting or noises. The patient is usually sitting completely free to choose his pose; he is even permitted to move about, if he so wishes. No third person is present, though we do not ascribe any particular significance to this fact as long as there is no interference.

However, we did once demonstrate waking suggestion in an auditorium, in the presence of about 200 university students who reacted rather noisily to both the procedure of suggestion and the behavior of the subjects. The young people were even permitted, during intermission, to ask them questions.

To avoid the possibility of transition of waking into sleep, the subjects should be told from time to time that they are fully awake, that they do not wish to sleep at all. Instead of speaking slowly and somewhat monotonously, as is the traditional procedure during hypnotizing, we address our subjects in a cheerful manner and sometimes in a commanding tone of voice. In other words, every measure is taken to avoid any overt semblance to hypnosis. It is necessary to say, however, that the subjects' posture, manners and ready orientation as to time, place and environment reveal beyond any doubt their waking, though somewhat subordinate, awareness.

To maintain continuous reactivity and sensitivity of the subjects, we employ certain verbal formulae. "Under the influence of suggestion," we say, "you have entered the state of complete dependence. But it is not sleep; in fact, you do not want to sleep at all and feel wide awake, fully aware of what happens around. You do not resist me and trust me, simply because you know that I shall never betray your trust. You will remain in this state of receptivity until I take you out of it. But in the meantime you will be extremely sensitive to my suggestions and instructions. Pay no attention to the people present here. Nothing bothers or annoys you. Indeed, you feel very well and think only of what I am saying."

In some instances, however, we do not even try to create the state of full dependence, but seek to produce directly some suggested phenomena worth investigating, for instance, catalepsy, amnesia, or hallucination.

Incidentally, most of our patients—they are mainly alcoholics and hysterics—have never been exposed to hypnotherapy and some of them have not previously heard of such method of treatment.

In conclusion, let us cite a couple of examples:

1. Patient G., twenty-six years of age, a victim of traumatic epilepsy. He was placed on a sofa, with his eyes open. He was repeatedly told that he was wide-awake and did not want to sleep. There were altogether three sessions of waking suggestion, separated by intervals of ten minute duration. At the end of each session various questions were asked.

*First suggestion.* The patient was told that he heard music and felt quite sad. His facial expression assumed the expression of sorrow and there appeared tears in his eyes. At the end of the session he related his experiences with plainly noticeable feeling.

*Second suggestion.* It was suggested to the patient that he just had a small glass of vodka (actually it was plain water). He downed the drink with an appropriate facial expression. Later on, while walking, he was unsteady on his feet.

*Third suggestion.* The patient was informed that his left hand was rising to touch his forehead and, no matter how hard he tried, it would remain in that position until he would be told to remove it. The suggestion was obeyed without any difficulty.

2. Patient P., forty-nine years of age. Diagnosis: chronic alcoholism. He never was subjected to hypnosis, but saw a few years before a demonstration of

it in a circus. The usual suggestion to be wide-awake was given.

*First suggestion.* The patient was told he was falling backward, and he did. Then he was told to clasp both hands together, and that he was unable to separate his fingers, no matter how hard he tried. He was unable to do anything about it, until permitted.

*Second suggestion.* The patient received the suggestion to form the so-called cataleptic bridge between two chairs. He later asserted that he felt so strong he could hold up the weight of a grown-up man.

# PART II

## *PSYCHOTHERAPY OF NEUROSES*

# THERAPEUTIC METHODOLOGY IN PSYCHASTHENIA

by E. K. Yakovleva

*(Leningrad)*

Much has been said and written concerning psychasthenia; but this literature expresses all kinds of views on its psychogenesis and offers many distinct methods of treatment, of which most impressive so far is psychotherapy. In disregarding what we believe to be wrong theories of the psychotherapy of neuroses, we wish to state that psychotherapy, as rooted in Pavlov's doctrine of the higher nervous activity, has received its scientific foundation only recently.

The complexity of the pathogenesis of psychasthenia calls for the use of fairly complicated techniques of treatment. Apart from nutritional and tonic medication, psychotherapy is the principal approach to this condition, and its main purpose is to clarify the circumstances of life underlying the development of the disease.

The method of psychotherapy used by us has been built around the genetic understanding of neuroses, as developed by V. N. Miassischev. It consists primarily

69

in the study of the patient's previous experience, insofar as it has bearing upon the development of his neurotic condition. "Man's experience," says V. N. Miassischev, "is determined by his attitudes toward reality; they are formed in the process of growth and maturation and play an important role in his subsequent actions and reactions to life."

This approach to psychotherapy underlies our treatment of psychasthenia; but in certain cases, depending on the form of the neurosis and its duration, it may be advantageous to turn to such supplementary methods as suggestion and hypnosis. Their use may be indicated, for instance, in the presence of high excitability or negativism, as shown by E. A. Popov.

A physician, employing psychotherapy built on the genetic interpretation of neuroses, examines first of all the patient's case history and clarifies within his own mind the peculiarities of the patient's character in his reactions to various circumstances of life and especially to the happenings serving as precipitating causes of the sickness. This information is supplied largely by the patient himself, but may be supplemented by his relatives. Nevertheless, such information does not quite suffice to determine the cause of the patient's disease. Consequently, the gathering of anamnestic data must not be merely formal; nor can it be limited to simple comments referring to certain events in the patient's life. More important is the clarification of his attitude toward each event relevant to his difficulties; and it is not so much the event itself that matters as the patient's interpretation of it. Indeed, it is this incorrect evaluation of events that is basically responsible for his subsequent troubles in life.

The physician's insight into the genesis of the case is not, by itself, of decisive significance in psychotherapy. It is much more important to make it possible for the patient himself to see and feel it correctly. By utilizing the contents of the patient's own anamnesis, particularly the motives for his specific actions, the physician is able to explain to him the hidden meaning of diverse pathogenic experiences, the causes of the resulting neurosis, and the origin of compulsion as a morbid but temporary symptom. In this connection, the doctor's authoritativeness is of considerable significance for, if properly used, it permits the patient actively to participate in the critical examination of his past actions and alternatives to them. When the rapport between the patient and the physician is thus established, the former is likely to provide some additional data, previously withheld or forgotten. This supplementary information indicates that the patient begins to comprehend the wrong nature of his habitual behavior. Such critical evaluation of episodes on the part of the patient and his increasing self-criticism toward the past and present conduct go a long way to examine his everyday difficulties rationally rather than emotionally and to find a way to better mental adjustment.

Evaluation of the causal factors in the development of a neurotic condition must never be conducted in a hurry; nor can a sufficient explanation growing out of thorough understanding of the pathogenesis of neurosis be replaced by premature comments. All aspects of treatment must be followed cautiously, so

71

that the patient himself would be able to appreciate it and receive it in the right spirit.

There is another way of saying this. Each process of psychotherapy has another side, that of a gradual re-education of the patient, leading him to the reconstruction of his emotionally-disturbed relations with the world into more wholesome and more satisfactory ones. This process of reconstruction, of altering the patient's habitual reactions can often be eminently successful, but never easy.

Re-education as a form of psychotherapy built around the patient's "practice of life," was advocated as early as P. B. Gannushkin. But it was V. M. Bekhterev who gave this method the name of "treatment by re-education." K. I. Platonov developed it a step farther by pointing out that it calls for precise recognition of the causes and conditions of the developing neurosis.

Of great importance in this process of re-education is self-education, that is to say, learning how to discipline oneself, to be critical of oneself, to regulate one's own conduct. This was clearly and explicitly stated for the first time by I. P. Pavlov who found that such self-understanding and self-control give the patient both a motive and opportunity to get adjusted to his surroundings.

The soundness of these views was frequently confirmed by our patients themselves after their recovery. One of them said, for instance, "All my life I was living by feelings and only now I have learned to reason." Another one wrote, "I am no longer a slave to my weaknesses. I am my own master, and I see everything in an entirely different light."

# PSYCHOTHERAPY IN PHOBIC STATES

## by A. M. Haletsky
### *(Astrakhan)*

The study of phobias brings out clearly the pathogenic role of isolated "sore points." Once the state of fear is formed under certain environmental conditions, the response is readily fixated in the form of pathological conditioning. This fact was often mentioned in the works of I. P. Pavlov, M. K. Petrova, A. G. Ivanov-Smolensky, B. N. Birman, E. A. Popov, N. P. Tatarenko, and others.

Some phobias are quite simple in their etiology. To this category belong the phobias of actors, lecturers and musicians who have to face a discriminating audience. This form of phobia usually originates in some failure of memorization causing the feeling of panic, "stoppage of thoughts" as well as excessive perspiration and pallor. Subsequently, on similar occasions, there arises fear that the failure may repeat itself. This expected reaction, unless overcome, becomes habitual and increases with the approach of the moment of responsibility. As a result, desired actions become inhibited, memory fails.

The following case will illustrate the problem.

Patient Y., born in 1929, a rhapsodist. In 1949, he was chided by a teacher in the school of music for a mistake in playing and told to restudy the assigned piece. But the next time the error occurred in the same place. The teacher became angry, declared that the student was doing this deliberately, and threatened to fail him unless the mistake was corrected. But the mistake occurred again and again, always in the same place, even while the student was practising at home. There appeared also sudden relaxations of fingers.

Psychotherapy resulted in a considerable improvement. The patient was able to play perfectly well by himself and before a familiar audience; he even participated in a group performance at a club. But he was never able to play the piece solo.

The task of eliminating such phobic inhibitions is by no means simple. The patients, in turning to a physician for help, usually are aware of the origin of the phobic symptom, but tend to minimize the pathogenic role of the original experience which, anyway, has in the meantime lost its significance.

Exercises along the same lines are not advisable, for they retain the same pathogenic power to cause excitement and inhibition. The patients must be told that attempts at vigorous self-control can be of no avail. Any practice should be preceded by systematic reduction of mental tension. It is well to recall in this connection K. S. Stanislavsky's advice found in his *My Life in Art*. All muscular tension, he said, must be eliminated by an actor about to come out on the stage. This isn't easy. Even a slight muscular tension interferes with freedom of motion, with adequate gestures. K. S. Stanislavsky justly urged elimination of "clamps" on the nerves.

The common fault of many actors, lecturers, musicians—of everybody suffering from the fear of memory failure or proper timing—consists in this, that all exercises, worrisome expectations, strenuous efforts to overcome the unhappy symptoms merely raise the state of tension which, in its turn, negatively stimulates cortical activities and interferes with normal automatisms. To eliminate such stubborn difficulties one should resort to exercises under relaxed domestic conditions. This is done in the following manner.

The patient sits down in a chair, making himself comfortable. His movements should be slowed down, while the muscles of his arms, legs and neck are permitted to relax. Thoughts in his head should also assume an even, unhurried character. As to emotions and volitions, they, too, should enter the state of relative ease and passivity. To forestall any possible disturbances, as in playing a musical instrument, the attitude of calmness must be gradually developed. No effort of will to meet an accidental difficulty or interference is permitted. Each activity, such as playing an instrument, rehearsal for a play, or reciting a poem, is consequently done only after a considerable preparation along the lines indicated above. One's attention must be entirely absorbed in living a role, in the sounds of a melody. If an actor happens to be forced by fear to abandon acting on the stage, he must go through all the steps of acting in front of his friends and acquaintances, children audiences or appearing in small clubs, before he permits himself to return to the stage. Prior to each appearance, he should again go through every means of freeing himself from worry or tension and reduce the vigor of his gestures and other motions. A lecturer is also urged to pay attention only to a few basic points of his speech and to talk calmly, slowly, avoiding loudness.

In talks with patients, the psychotherapist tries to explain the significance of psychasthenic reactions in the origin of phobia and shows the ways of strengthening one's will and self-confidence by utilizing examples taken from the patient's own life. The physician comments also upon the formation of pathological conditioned links and upon the mechanism of inert irradiation. To be effective, he must always have a sufficient supply of convincing examples and arguments.

Psychotherapeutic action is somewhat more complex in phobias originating in inner conflicts which in their turn are caused by a clash of stimulating and inhibiting processes within the patient's personality. Unfortunately, this problem has never been sufficiently studied, perhaps because it readily reminds us of the psychoanalytic theory of repression.

Simple methods of psychotherapy are even less likely to succeed in phobias of hypochondriacal type. Such patients may be afraid to go out after dark because of occasional giddiness, attacks of tachycardia, or because they suffer from nyctophobia.

A careful study of the ailment may show, in such cases, a chronic infection leading to various autonomic disturbances. Repeated temperature measurements may show a slight fever. The patients may complain of chills, excessive perspiration, periodic weakness, loss of weight, recurrent colds, insomnia. Quite often the source of such troubles lies in chronic tonsillitis.

Any psychotherapeutic measures must go in these cases together with antibiotic or antiallergic medication. The idea should be given up that every complaint of a neurotic is necessarily psychogenic in origin. The possibility of a somatic background of certain neuroses, among them of phobias, is often overlooked by the psychiatrists. As a matter of fact, the patients should sometimes be told of the possible interrelationship between somatic illness and psychogenic symptoms, for there are now and then organic reasons for excessive fears and unrealistic expectations. This helps the patient, anyway, to trust his doctor a little more and enables him to understand the purpose of the treatment.

The patient with psychogenic somatic disturbances is particularly sensitive toward what his physician does or prescribes. He resents the advice of a doctor saying "not to worry about internal sensations" or "to stop thinking about his health," for all this is presumably nothing but nervousness. He sometimes leaves the physician with the feeling that his experiences and feelings were disregarded.

Psychotherapy can never be limited to several uniform patterns of treatment, such as persuasion, suggestion, hypnosis, and the like. Forms of neuroses are rich in variety. Equally rich should be the available methods of psychotherapy and their combinations.

# THERAPY OF CERTAIN FORMS OF HYSTERIA
by Z. A. Kopil-Levina
*(Novosibirsk)*

Therapeutic problems in certain functional disorders of sensations and speech have never been sufficiently investigated. As a matter of fact, there still are a few old-fashioned physicians retaining the unwarranted attitude toward such patients as peculiar and unsociable characters.

We have had an opportunity to study quite a number of these patients, some with disturbances of long duration, who have not yielded to ordinary methods of psychotherapy. Our observations have been conducted on 377 clinical cases and ninety-seven experimental cases. As late as December, 1941, we proposed that the general disturbance of skin sensitivity around the defective sense organ be regarded as a definite diagnostic sign of functional disturbance. Thus, in full deafness of both ears one often observes the anesthetic condition of the conchae; in partial deafness hypesthesia may accompany it. In cases of one-sided deafness anesthesia or hypesthesia are likely to be confined to the corresponding ear.

In persons suffering from mutism, the tongue, lips and portions of the throat may be affected with anesthesia or hypesthesia. Similar phenomena may go with aphonia.

The same rule has been found to apply to normal people subjected to experimental hypnosis with induced deafness, mutism, dysphonia, blindness, blepharospasm, concentric narrowing of the field of vision, and also paralyses. Similar findings have also been made by G. V. Gershuni and his collaborators (1945) and A. M. Andreyev (1947). Practically identical observations made on the deaf-and-mute were related by V. A. Guiliarovsky in his *Old and New Problems of Psychiatry.*

Loss of skin sensitivity in the relevant region is regarded by us as highly significant not only for diagnosis but also for the treatment of all functional disturbances of the sense organs, speech, and kinesthesis.

Our method of stimulation consists in a series of skin-pricks moving gradually from the points with normal sensitivity to regions of the lost or reduced skin sensitivity; from time to time this approaching movement is replaced by side movements. Such stimulation may be performed in the state of hypnosis as well as in the waking state. In either case we usually observe gradual restoration of skin sensitivity together with the restoration of hearing in the patients suffering from functional deafness; or, as the case may be, of sight in the patients suffering from functional blindness.

In cases of functional disturbances of speech, such as mutism, aphonia, and stuttering, we modify the traditional logopedic exercises consisting in gradual

79

transition from pronouncing separate sounds to pronouncing syllables, words, and phrases. Our method replaces this procedure with one conducted in the state of hypnotic sleep; or else, following the way of Bernheim and Bekhterev, the patient is placed in a lying position with closed eyes and in darkness. As a result, the full restoration of speech is usually achieved in one or two sessions. In cases of mutism accompanied by the disruption of the entire speech mechanism in the form of adynamia (insufficient movement of the tongue and mouth muscles, together wih analgesia), we seldom succeed in bringing about pronunciation of sounds or syllabi through a simple verbal command. But we do attain this purpose by opening the patient's mouth and asking him to utter the first vowel sound by taking a deep breath and exhaling, and by shaping the lips in a proper way. This addition of tactile and motor components to sounds results usually in quick restoration of speech.

In cases of the deaf-and-dumb, we first restore hearing and then speech. The same order of succession is followed also in dysphonia and stuttering combined with deafness.

In every instance of disturbance of hearing, the method of stimulation, as described above, proved to be beneficial in the first session. Return of speech in mutism and dysphonia required one or two sessions; and correction of stuttering called for as many as three or four sessions.

This method has been found effective also in the work of other specialists—psychiatrists, neuropathologists, otolaryngologists, ophthalmologists, among them A. S. Chistovich and O. I. Shershevskaya.

Let us consider the following case.

80

Patient G., twelve years of age, had poor vision for several years. He was given eyeglasses and had to sit in the first row at school. In 1949 he developed inflammation of the eyelids; as a result, he became practically blind. He no longer could read, write, or even recognize objects; he had to grope to move about. When transferred from a Novosibirsk hospital to our clinic, the boy underwent a careful examination. We discovered analgesia exactly corresponding in form to the glasses. No organic damage to either the organs of vision or the nervous system could be detected. The diagnosis was: hysterical blindness. The boy's eyesight was fully regained when the analgesic region was restored to sensitivity by stimulation. Catamnesis for several years remained positive.

### CONCLUSIONS:

1. Anesthesia in the peripheral region of sensory organs, when it follows the loss of their function, appears to be a definite diagnostic sign of a functional and consequently correctible disturbance usually arising as a result of inertia of protective inhibitions.

2. In functional disorders of the sensory organs, speech, paralyses and contractures of limbs, we can recommend the method of functional restoration of the affected sense organs by means of arousing the sensitivity of their peripheral parts.

81

# COMBINATION OF PSYCHOTHERAPY WITH
# MEDICINAL SLEEP

## by O. R. Chitava
### (Tbilisi)

Individual psychotherapy, as the basic method in the treatment of neuroses, must be built around three factors: qualities of the patient's personality, the form of his illness, and its causes.

The specific feature of human neuroses, according to I. P. Pavlov, is the involvement of the secondary signal system. It plays a major role in the origin and progress of the disease, in some cases retarding its development, in others accelerating it.

K. I. Platonov's experiments have demonstrated that verbal suggestion may alter the metabolic processes and activities of the internal organs. Speech therapy (A. G. Ivanov-Smolensky) is the outgrowth of these ideas.

Starting from the principle of combination treatment of neuroses and availing ourselves of A. D. Zurabashvili's suggestion, we subjected twenty patients to psychotherapy combined with extended night sleep. The patients in this group suffered from neuroses of

82

the following types: hysteria, psychasthenia, phobias, hypochondriac syndromes, and compulsions. The duration of their sickness ranged from one month to two years.

After a careful clinical examination, an individual regimen was prescribed to each patient. Assuming that every neurotic condition has both psychogenic and somatic components, medication treatment (glucose, vitamines, strychnine, etc.) was prescribed in all cases to strengthen the organism. On the first day of treatment, the physician conducted an explanatory talk on varieties of nervous sickness, its causes and therapy.

Psychotherapy began only after a full contact, including mutual trust, was established between the physician and his patient. The choice of treatment depended on the nature of the disease, patient's age and his intellectual and cultural characteristics. To prolong night sleep, barbiturates were used. The length of night sleep varied from ten to twelve hours. The whole treatment continued from two to three weeks.

The following variations of treatment with extended sleep were used:

1. Medicinal sleep for several days, followed by psychotherapy. This variation was employed whenever the element of inhibition was conspicuous in the clinical picture (for instance, in phobias and hypochondriasis).

2. Medicinal sleep preceded by a few sessions of psychotherapy to weaken neurotic symptoms and to quiet the patient down. This sort of treatment was used in hysteria and general excitability.

3. The two methods of treatment conducted simultaneously to the end.

The combination method of treatment on the background of extended night sleep proved to be most successful in psychasthenia, compulsions, hypochondriasis, and some forms of phobia. In cases of hysteria, when the patient's activities were at a low level, medicinal sleep was alternated with waking suggestion or hypnosis.

The treatment had a marked positive effect in fourteen cases. Noticeable improvement was observed in a few instances after two or three days.

The success of psychotherapy combined with extensive night sleep can be explained in this way: Under the influence of sleep, there is strengthening of the protective forces of the organism, leading to a better tonus of the nervous system. These changes create favorable opportunities for psychotherapy. Relevant suggestion, under such conditions, makes it possible to stimulate certain areas of the cortex; this seems to precipitate negative irradiation thus helping to weaken the pathogenic centers of excitability.

# THE METHOD OF INDIRECT SUGGESTION
## AS USED IN HYSTERIA

### by Y. L. Schreiber
#### (Leningrad)

We use a form of indirect suggestion psychotherapy to remove the fixated symptoms of hysteria, otherwise unyielding to ordinary methods.

A week before treatment starts, the patient is
informed at considerable length that his illness is
functional in character, distinguished by conversion
phenomena. The patient is assured, however, that he
is to be treated in a manner that will be of considerable help. After spending several days in expectation
of the "medication" intended to remove the symptoms
of his ailment, the patient is conducted to the treatment room and invited to lie down on a couch. He is
then informed that the "medicine" will be poured
slowly on a special mask and assimilated by his
organism by means of breathing in the evaporating
drug. He is furthermore assured that the substance
brings no unpleasant reactions whatsoever, such as
nausea or headache. These remarks help considerably
to avoid any possible complications arising in auto-

suggestion. The patient is then told, in a manner well adjusted to the level of his education, that he will feel much better, that the symptoms of his disease are a product of cortical inhibition and that the drug, being a powerful stimulating substance, is intended to remove the inhibition. It is explained, for instance, that the patient's hyperkinesis is determined by excitation of brain cells, and that the drug, by calming the nervous system, puts them back into a normal state.

Immediately after this, a registered nurse begins to pour, drop by drop, some aromatic liquid, such as menthol dissolved in alcohol, on the mask already on the patient's face. The whole procedure of treatment takes no more than ten minutes. In the meantime, a discussion is conducted with some other physician concerning the effectiveness of the treatment, with which the latter concurs. They point out that the drug has an excellent effect upon the nervous system and is capable of removing many pathological manifestations. No remarks are addressed directly to the patient; from the very beginning of the treatment he remains a passive listener to the conversation conducted only between the two physicians: the conversation is actually a question of indirect suggestion.

This method of treatment has been used by us for a great variety of symptoms, including hysterical contracture, hyperkinesis, partial paralysis, astasia-abasia, mutism, and persistent vomiting.

Whereas in other forms of psychotherapy the authority of the physician is of great importance, if seen in the totality of relations between himself and his patient, in the method of indirect suggestion there are additional elements of autosuggestion—the patient's faith in the effective character of the "medication;" "expectant attention" (V. M. Bekhterev's term), and "readiness" to reaction on the part of the patient's nervous system.

It is obvious, consequently, that the greater is the patient's eagerness to get rid of the fixated symptom, the quicker comes the curative effect and the more lasting it is. In some instances, however, it becomes necessary practically to repeat the whole procedure so as to extend and consolidate the attainment. But whatever be the case, every time, immediately after the mask is removed, the patient is told to do a lot of practice in the region of the removed symptom; that is to say, to talk a lot after the correction of mutism, to get up and sit down again and again after overcoming paralysis.

The social atmosphere surrounding the patient is quite important, too, in this connection. His environment at the hospital is formed not only by the medical personnel involved in the preparations and follow-up activities of indirect suggestion therapy, but also by other patients, insofar as he looks eagerly forward to favorable results of the treatment.

The medical personnel assisting in the work must be specially trained. Nurses, for instance, must be instructed in the physiological mechanisms of medicinal action as well as in the psychology of suggestibility and its relation to forming normal conditioned responses.

The method of indirect suggestion psychotherapy is indicated whenever the so-called deep and prolonged therapy is not feasible and whenever it is important to remove pathological symptoms without delay. This method has been in use since 1939-40 when it was first applied to a grave case of hyperkinesis.

Most patients, on completion of the treatment, react strongly to the restoration of the lost function; some of them become even euphoric as the emotional background of experience enters the stage of reconstruction. In some instances, patients fall asleep for several hours almost immediately after removal of the mask, apparently under the influence of the exhaustive emotional experience and protective inhibitions. This sleep seems to normalize basic neural processes and to raise the functional power of cortical cells.

In quite a few cases of cured hysterical paralysis or astasia-abasia, the patients develop moderate pains in the extremities on completion of treatment; but, considering the previous condition of a long duration, this seems to be rather natural. These pain sensations usually last for one to ten days, their duration being roughly proportional to the duration of the pathological state. To prevent this complication, we employ massage of the limbs prior to the treatment.

An important question of principle must not be disregarded in connection with this method of indirect suggestion therapy. To what extent is medical ethics compatible with the use of an indifferent substance while it is supposed to be a valuable medication?

In each concrete case, the physician must decide for himself as to the method of treatment. In indirect suggestion therapy, the physician's words are of great and real benefit to the patient. Is it right to abstain from uttering them? Is it right to leave the patient sick when he can be cured? Moreover, if the gravely sick individuals must be told nothing but truth, they are needlessly burdened with iatrogeny.

# ON THE PSYCHOTHERAPY OF
# PSYCHOGENIC IMPOTENCE

## by I. M. Apter
### *(Kharkov)*

By psychogenic impotence we understand various functional disturbances of the activity of the male sexual organs, expressing themselves in the loss, weakening or some other deviation from the normal reflex processes controlling erection and ejaculation.

There were altogether 220 patients of this kind under our observation. The great majority of them (89%) were in the age group between twenty and forty. More than half of them (126) were married, the rest (94) were not.

The total clinical picture, when broken down by symptoms, may be represented as follows:

| *Functional disturbance* | *Number of cases* |
|---|---|
| Loss or weakness of the reflex of erection | 115 |
| Inhibited erection and ejaculatio praecox | 65 |
| Normal erection and ejaculatio praecox | 28 |
| Loss of erection and sexual indifference | 7 |
| Psychic aspermatism | 5 |

Quite a few of the patients developed disturbance of sexual activity clearly on a general neurotic basis. A number of them enjoyed a period of satisfactory sexual relations in the past; three men were married happily for a number of years, complaining of no previous impotence. But, on the whole, every one of the patients acknowledged some inadequacies of *his* sexual experience.

Most patients had but a single symptom of sexual inadequacy. In the common background of neurosis there was much masturbation in adolescence and youth, extensive and recurrent fears of venereal disease, continual practice of coitus interruptus during the marriage period. Several patients had to share their room with married couples and apparently did not feel sexually at ease.

Let us now briefly consider the problem of medical treatment. The principal method of handling cases of psychogenic impotence is, of course, psychotherapy. More specifically, explanation and persuasion must be used extensively; in cases of persistent worries, some technique of distraction may be advisable.

But the choice of treatment is never easy. Many factors have to be considered: the characteristics of impotence, etiology, individual peculiarities of the patient's organism, the state of his health. In some cases, the measures amount only to protective therapy; in other cases, they aim at stimulation.

In this connection, our own patients were extensively exposed to waking suggestion; in some instances the state of drowsiness was preferred. The method of hypnosis was employed but seldom. Some physiotherapy and pharmacotherapy was used concurrently.

The most important thing in all the cases was, however, to give the patient the strong feeling of confidence that he had indeed a good chance of recovery. The patient's first encounter with the physician was always of paramount significance. For the patient invariably looked forward to meeting the doctor with eagerness, worry and hope. And the physician could give him assurance of hope only after a careful and complete somatic, urological, neurological, and endocrinological examination.

The following rules had always to be remembered in the choice of the psychotherapeutic method. Whenever the patient assumed that his impotence had been caused by masturbation during adolescence, he had to be reassured and informed that the habit was actually quite harmless. He had to be told also that occasional and temporary failures of sexual life are by no means rare among healthy people, and that only his suggestibility as well as ignorance gave him the false impression that he was unfit for normal sexual life. He had to be told that only these fears rather than previous masturbation were responsible for the inhibition of his sexual reflexes.

In the cases when the patient had not yet discontinued masturbation, it was necessary to help him get rid of the habit, and then to strengthen his sexual reflexes. To do so, it was advantageous to employ the method of explanation, persuasion, and waking suggestion.

When impotence was connected with the practice of coitus interruptus, the physician urged the patient immediately to discontinue the undesirable practice, to give some rest to overexcited sexual centers, and

91

to abstain from sexual relations for about two or three months. No stimulants whatsoever were permitted during the period.

We employed waking suggestion therapy in cases where sexual approach was accompanied by fears and worries, and tried to instill self-confidence in the patient. If it was known that some highly irritating factor was responsible for impotence in the first place, we arranged for a psychotherapeutic talk to explain to the patient the physiological mechanism of his weakness and to recommend proper counter-measures.

If the cause of impotence happened to be connected with a change in the habits of cohabitation, it was recommended temporarily to change the environment, for instance, to take a trip.

Quite often it was found useful to arrange a talk with the patient's wife in his presence, during which the physician might comment upon the temporary character of all psychogenic ailments, an excellent chance of recovery, and also upon the vital role of the wife's conduct in the progress of recovery.

On the whole, the process of treatment of patients with psychogenic impotence may be analytically separated into several stages, namely:

1. The first meeting: a frank talk between the physician and his patient to calm the latter down; suggestion of confidence in the likely recovery.

2. Removal of the emotion of fear in an approach to a woman.

3. Protective psychotherapy, stimulating therapy, or distracting therapy.

4. Availing himself of a convenient moment, the physician finds an opportunity to test the results of

the treatment, as seen in the light of the patient's condition and surrounding environment.

Psychotherapy of psychogenic impotence demands much effort from the physician, examination of minute details in the case history; it calls also for much patience and persistence on the part of both the physician and the patient.

Positive results are not expected in all instances. In the group observed by us, there was complete recovery in fifty-six percent of the cases and a definite improvement in twenty-three percent.

# PSYCHOTHERAPY IN THE
## MEDICO-PEDAGOGIC PRACTICE OF
## A CHILD PSYCHIATRIST

### by N. G. Veshapelli
### (Tbilisi)

It must be regretfully admitted that the role of psychotherapy is not sufficiently appreciated in the field of the medico-pedagogic activity of the physicians working around the schools and trying to prevent or treat neurotic ailments. It ought to be remembered, in this connection, that the peculiarities of the cortical neurodynamics of a growing organism make the children's nervous system highly sensitive to endogenous traumata arising in family troubles, errors of upbringing, over-exertion, and the like.

Our physiologists have demonstrated a close relationship between functions of the nervous system and those of internal organs, and this is particularly obvious during childhood. Consequently, various somatic grievances, such as infections and toxic conditions, have intimate bearing upon functional changes in the nervous system of children.

Children who had the misfortune of suffering at an

early age from diseases of the brain (meningitis, encephalitis, traumatic injuries, etc.), that is, children who have some inadequacy of the nervous system, however inconspicuous it may be to outsiders, are ready victims of neurotic conditions, especially when there is no one around to take psychoprophylactic, psychohygienic, and psychotherapeutic measures.

It is the job of physicians of every specialization working with children to be trained and skilful in recognizing and comprehending the initial signs of neurotic disturbances, including those assuming the form of various compensatory mechanisms. To fulfill this obligation, it is sometimes necessary to subject children to detailed study. In doing so, the physician must not fail to consider family conditions, the mode of living, and the children's environment. The basic and most sound rule of medico-prophylactic work among children has been explicitly stated by I. P. Pavlov, according to whom the organism and the surrounding milieu are inseparably interrelated. The medico-prophylactic task of every pediatrician and every child psychiatrist is, in short, to promote and regulate normal relations between the somato-biological state of each child's organism and the content and requirements of his immediate environment.

A healthy young organism and the properly organized environment (home, family, school, etc.), a well-planned working day, and, above all, absence of any emotionally negative, harm-inducing experiences constitute a wholesome setting for the life of children. Under these conditions there is no room for any breakdown of cortical neural processes or for formation of neurotic conditions.

It happens now and then, however, that the close

tie between the child's organism and demands of his surroundings somehow break down. The lowered responsiveness of the child, asthenization of his organism as a result of a series of illnesses, or organically determined functional inadequacy of the nervous system lead to reduced adjustability of his organism to ordinary requirements of everyday environment. Wrong conditions of home education, unusual pressure imposed upon his leisure time—as when the parents insist that the child, in addition to routine school studies, should also go to a school of music, even though he manifests no inclination for it—interfere with his peace of mind. All this is likely to undermine the pattern of his habits, reduce efficiency, create fear of failing in examinations, loss of self-confidence, and emotional tensions. There may arise in this way malfunction of his brain centers and eventually a neurotic condition.

That is why child psychiatrists as well as teachers may play a very important role in the timely recognition of early symptoms of a neurosis, serving as signals of an unsatisfactory state of the child's mental health.

Every child, overwhelmed by impressions of the day, should sleep a sufficient number of hours every night so as to provide the cortex of his brain with a normal amount of rest. For sleep, as a source of protective inhibition, is of very special significance in supplying prophylactic measures to combat neurotic dangers.

A rational order of the daily routine, individually adjusted and differentiated, improvement in family conditions of life, normalization of cortical processes, and balancing of organic health and environmental stimuli and reactions—all these lie at the foundation of the medico-prophylactic activity of the child psychotherapist.

The main purpose of psychotherapy consists, as correctly pointed out by V. A. Guiliarovsky, V. N. Miassischev, G. E. Sukharev, and T. N. Simpson, not so much in getting rid of neurotic symptoms themselves as in re-education, with gradual elimination of traits conducive to the formation of neuroses. At the same time we want considerable improvement in the conditions of study, mode of life, and bodily exercise.

It follows, in general, that an efficient organization of psychotherapeutic help to school children must be made everywhere a part of practical work of all medico-prophylactic and pedagogical institutions.

# PSYCHOTHERAPY OF CHILD STUTTERING

## by N. A. Vlassova
### (Moscow)

There are many different views on the nature of stuttering and the proper methods of its treatment. Nevertheless, however different be the interpretations, most authors agree that stuttering stems basically from a neurosis. Even the authors who used to regard it as a local cramp treat it in their later works as neurotic in origin. Practically all psychiatrists take the same position.

It is necessary to acknowledge that in every available method of treatment of stuttering, with the possible exception of surgery, one invariably finds elements of psychotherapy. They are found even among the proponents of the didactic method, who support their endless breathing and voice exercises with talks and recorded advices exemplified by "Be calm, bold and wakeful."

Stuttering has been regarded as a neurosis for the last thirty years, and its treatment consists overwhelmingly in psychotherapeutic talks.

V. A. Guiliarovsky contends that "psychotherapy

is a system of mental influences trying to avail itself of the principle of the unity of soma and psyche, that is, of the unity of the organism and its environment, in order to obtain favorable results in the patient's condition." This definition of psychotherapy is in full agreement with the medico-pedagogical work we do with the children suffering from stuttering.

Proceeding from the assumption that no personality can be seriously regarded as isolated from its environment, we maintain that an organized group of children suffering from stuttering provides the most favorable factors for the re-education, not only of the child's speech, but also of his entire personality.

The following case illustrates the point.

Irene began to stutter at the age of four; she had hardly spoken at all before she was three, but with speech came also stuttering. Her parents, particularly the father, were in panic and turned for help from one doctor to another; and following a physician's advice they completely isolated the girl from any contact with other children. Irene was growing utterly capricious and spoiled. The father was obeying, to keep her from crying, every one of her whims; the mother, trying to moderate Irene's demands, was not even permitted to educate the child. The girl was growing more and more despotic. Stuttering increased to the point when the question arose whether she should go to school at all. Then the parents were compelled to visit a speech clinic in the local hospital. At that time the girl was seven years of age; her stuttering was bad, but even worse was her conduct, particularly with regard to her mother.

In the clinic she met an entirely different situation. Every good or bad action on the part of the children was discussed; but, most surprisingly, Irene did not appear to mind it at all. Instead of objecting to visits to the clinic, she eagerly awaited them. Within a week she whispered to one of the supervisors that she would like to be praised by the group. Having been told that every praise must be deserved, the girl changed her conduct even at home. Her behavior toward the mother improved remarkably, and she was finally lauded by the group. At the same time her speech began rapidly to improve. In the course of time, Irene graduated from the school and, eventually, from the Institute of Architecture. She never stuttered again.

Sympathetic talks within a group go a long way to overcome both stuttering and the fears that underlie it. An opportunity to speak, without stuttering, to other children during games is so attractive to a neurotic child that visits to the supervised group become more and more desirable; and, for that reason, the effectiveness of this treatment increases.

Another psychotherapeutic activity which makes speech easier for the child consists in musical rhythmical exercises, known as logorhythmic and introduced by V. A. Guiliarovsly. During these exercises speech is combined with music and motions. A child, in listening to music together with other children, does not pay much attention to speech and is thus enabled to utter words without self-consciousness.

Let us make one more remark in conclusion. The psychotherapeutic activities with children suffering from stuttering consist not only in special talks, which may be somewhat difficult for preschool children to understand, but also in various positive influences of the entire group of children, in the re-education of children through a mentally suitable environment, and in the professional organization of the entire medico-pedagogic process of speech reconstruction.

If every physician has to be a psychotherapist of a sort, so has every specialist in speech who encounters stuttering children. It is well known, indeed, that a clumsily worded question, a careless remark, or a thoughtless answer may do considerable damage to the sensitive psychology of the sick.

Thus we come to see that psychotherapy when used with children suffering from stuttering is much more than a mere verbal technique: It is a whole system of measures designed to achieve health and personality improvement among children with a real difficulty.

PART III

*PSYCHOTHERAPY OF PSYCHOSES*

# THE ROLE OF PSYCHOTHERAPY IN THE TREATMENT OF PSYCHOSES

## by N. V. Kantorovich
### *(Frunze)*

In spite of the fact that the psychiatrists have been taking a very active part in the study of theoretical and practical problems of psychotherapy, the main areas of its application have been so far neuroses, alcoholisms, narcomania, psychoprophylaxis of child-birth, certain somatic ailments, etc. As to psychoses in the narrower sense of the word, the psychiatrists do not use much psychotherapy or any special psycho-therapeutic methodologies in the treatment of their patients, though they do attribute considerable signif-icance to the psychotherapeutic effect of the regimen of mental hospitals, their surroundings, and personnel relations with the patients.

In the study of periodic disturbances of such patients, it has been definitely established that among the immediate causes of any excitement and the general deterioration of the patient morale, words uttered by the personnel and inmates play an appre-ciable and sometimes unhappy role. It follows that, if improper verbal influence can cause deterioration in the condition of mental patients or evoke the appearance of new symptoms, then proper speech therapy may certainly be of curative value.

The principal method in the psychotherapy of psychoses is that of persuasion and explanation. But we should not confuse persuasion with waking suggestion in this connection. Though persuasion cannot possibly exclude every element of suggestion, there is a substantial difference between the two methods. In waking suggestion as well as in hypnosis, the physician employs categorical or imperative patterns of speech, whereas in persuasion he discusses with the patient what is of interest to the latter and uses rational arguments, logic, scientific facts, and the like. All this becomes quite obvious when one encounters patients who are open to persuasion without being in the least suggestible, or the other way around. As to the treatment by suggestion, it is on the whole preferable to use hypnotic suggestion than waking one, for the latter is much weaker by comparison and has few advantages of its own. Unfortunately, however, quite a few psychotic patients cannot be hypnotized at all because of their low suggestibility. Nevertheless, hypnotherapy has been successfully applied in psychiatric practice, for instance, in the removal of hallucinations. The principle is simple enough: if it is possible to produce hallucinations in normal persons by means of hypnosis, then surely it must be possible to remove them in the sick by the same means.

Let us consider the following case:

Patient A., nineteen years of age. Diagnosis: hashish addiction. From 1952 to 1955 the patient smoked hashish systematically, adding it to tobacco. Beginning with June, 1955, he began to experience frequent auditory hallucinations, considerably enhanced by the use of the narcotic. From time to time he heard voices telling him of various things, sometimes giving orders. There were also a few mild visual hallucinations. His emotional disposition became extremely unstable. From September 29th to October 10th, 1955, the subject was subjected to hypnotherapy; there were thirteen sessions altogether. During that period he had a few hallucinations, but they were weak and vague. Four days after the conclusion of hypnotherapy, however, auditory hallucinations returned in their original strength. Apparently, the effect of hypnosis could be merely incomplete and temporary.

Even though hypnosis can be advantageously employed in psychoses, the principal method of psychotherapy in such cases is the method of persuasion. Our experience indicates that a course of psychotherapeutic treatment should go through four successive stages.

The first or preliminary stage permits the physician to get acquainted and establish a contact with the patient by means of talks dealing with matters of interest to the latter, without touching upon anything pertaining to his pathological experiences. During these sessions (two will suffice) the physician learns a great deal about prominent traits of the patient's personality, while the latter becomes adjusted to the presence of his doctor.

The purpose of the second stage is to help the patient assume the right attitude toward his sickness and develop the feeling of trust toward his physician. No more than three sessions will be needed to attain this goal.

107

The third and most important stage of persuasion psychotherapy deals with altering the conduct and experiences of the patient. Much depends here on the patient. According to our observations, in some cases three or four talks will suffice, whereas in other cases as many as twenty talks will be required. They can be conducted daily, every second day, or with larger intervals. Each talk should last anywhere from ten to forty minutes.

We do not believe, to be sure, that it is possible to cure psychoses merely by psychotherapy. But we do find that, even when used by itself, it may lead to considerable improvement in the patient's symptoms, response to treatment, and general cooperativeness. Moreover, in combination with insulin shock, electro-shock treatment, or sleep therapy, psychotherapy may substantially increase the effectiveness of these types of therapy.

To make this clear, let us cite a case:

Patient F., twenty-three years of age. Diagnosis: traumatic psychosis. The illness developed quickly on September 10th, 1955, immediately after an automobile accident without any visible bodily injury. When the patient regained consciousness, he showed anterograde amnesia, emotional instability, tendency toward inner conflicts. He acted rudely, demanded immediate discharge. Among other symptoms were: poor orientation, suspiciousness, euphoria, confabulation.

Treatment: prolonged sleep, injections of magnesium sulphide. The patient reacted readily to persuasion; aware of his illness, he conceded the faults of his conduct and developed an attitude of confidence toward the medical personnel. There were altogether eight psychotherapeutic talks.

The patient was discharged after seventeen days in the hospital without any signs of psychosis.

It is true, of course, that acute traumatic psychoses may occasionally disappear by themselves, without any psychotherapy, within this period. But it is important to point out that the patient reacted positively to psychotherapy from the very beginning and because of this made easier his relations with the personnel thus enabling them to introduce symptomatic medical treatment.

The fourth and final stage of psychotherapy, in these cases, consists in consolidation of the attained therapeutic remission as well as in preparation of the patient's attitudes for the post-psychotic period. This stage implies resumption of employment, restoration of temporarily lost interests, real life contacts, etc. To this stage, too, we ascribe considerable importance. For it is well known that many patients, having recovered from psychotic symptoms, find themselves overwhelmed with passivity, desolation, fears, and asthenia. As long as these patients are free from any organic injury, they often react quite well to psychotherapeutic persuasion, provided it is conducted cautiously and patiently.

Let us examine another clinical case:

Patient G., twenty years of age. Diagnosis: a simple form of schizophrenia, second commitment. During the five months of his commitment he was treated with prolonged sleep, medication (caffeine, phenamine, glutamine acid), and a combination of

109

insulin shocks and electro-shock treatments (twenty-seven of the former and three of the latter). At the end of this period, the patient was still indifferent, taciturn, lacking in initiative, inactive. All questions were answered correctly but briefly. He was spending hours without doing anything. All work, reading and playing were declined with the remark, "It does not interest me."

Sessions of psychotherapy were introduced at that time. The talks emphasized this line of argument: during the course of treatment the patient got accustomed to inactivity and gradually lost typical interests of a normal man of good health; to change this trend, it is necessary to re-activate contacts with the outside world, to resume work and reading, however difficult it may be at first; when this is done, old habitual ties will revive. This form of persuasion proved to be quite successful. The patient turned somewhat reluctantly to reading, chessplay, and conversation with other patients. He spontaneously confessed one day that talks with the physician were helpful. The sphere of his interests and activities gradually enlarged, and he was soon discharged considerably improved.

Among the tasks of the last stage of psychotherapy is either a critical analysis of the patient's state of health or an intimate discussion of his pathological experiences during the sickness. This can be done, to be sure, only when there is no amnesia of the acute period of the psychosis. The significance of such discussions has been well expressed by one patient with recurrent schizophrenia: "It is not the first time that I have been sick, but it is the first time that, at the time of discharge, I have understood what has happened to me. Previously, I was leaving the hospital, as it were, in a daze: my condition improved, but why and how I had no idea; so I decided to remember nothing and to think of nothing. But now my head is clear and I know and understand a great deal about my illness."

What remains to be done is to examine the question concerning indications or counterindications of psychotherapy for the mentally sick. With regard to hypnotherapy we can say from personal experience that it is indicated in cases of depression and hypomanic states, hallucinosis, hypochondriac syndromes, psychogenic stupor, pseudodementia, and epileptic dysphoria. It is counterindicated in cases of lowered suggestibility and in the presence of delirium.

Psychotherapy of persuasion has a much greater field of application. The only counterindication, properly speaking, is when it is impossible to establish contact with the patient. In other words, it is advisable except when there is deep disturbance of consciousness, extreme psychomotor excitement, deep stupor, or advanced feeblemindedness.

Psychotherapy of persuasion can be employed in paranoid, hallucinatory, depressive and hypomanic states, hypochondriac syndromes, mild amentic states, delirium in the periods of clear consciousness. The best results are obtained with the following: reactive psychoses, post-traumatic, post-infectional and manic-depressive states, some forms of schizophrenia (particularly paranoid) and epilepsy, early stages of senility, and somatogenic psychoses. The undeniable merit of this method lies in the absence of any complications.

Insofar as psychotherapy is generally insufficient

111

to achieve by itself any cure of psychosis, it should be conducted in combination with physiotherapy and medications. It is particularly significant in connection with insulin-shock treatment; at that time, the patients become more accessible, their pathological experiences become stabilized; their nervous systems, too, show a tendency toward normalization. Psychotherapy administered during that state is able to strengthen and consolidate whatever improvements have resulted. Our observations show, however, that when such treatment is conducted "mechanically," when the physician watches only the patient's somatic condition, the success of the treatment is statistically lower than when psychotherapy is applied intelligently and with interest.

It must be conceded, of course, that psychotherapy does not always produce positive results. But we can say, though as yet without exact figures, that positive results are achieved in the majority of cases.

## ON THE PSYCHOTHERAPY OF
## SCHIZOPHRENIA

by A. N. Molokhov
*(Kishinev)*

Psychotherapy is hardly used at all in the treatment
of schizophrenia. The reason for that lies probably
in the traditional attitude of shocked passivity toward
this mental disease. Many unsuccessful attempts to
apply active psychotherapy to acute states of schizophrenia may have aggravated the situation still
further. But the main obstacle to the use of psychotherapy in schizophrenic cases has lain since the
beginning of the century in the psychoanalytic approach to the understanding of pathology of the mind.
Much useless terminology has been coined and much
unscientific work has been done in efforts to remove
"repressions" and thus to restore the patient's contact
with reality.

Such misconceptions arise from insufficient com-
prehension of acute or chronic forms of schizophrenia.
It is also often forgotten that, if psychological traumata sometimes contribute to the schizophrenic proc-

113

ess, it does not necessarily follow that psychotherapy can readily reverse this pathological process.

Schizophrenia causes in its development considerable qualitative changes in human psychology, undermines the basic rules of one's logic, and modifies one's social attitudes to such an extent as to make a person virtually unrecognizable. That is why it takes considerable knowledge and skill to deal effectively with a patient suffering from this disease.

Some authors consider it possible, however, to retard or even to stop the development of schizophrenia by means of active psychotherapy, at least in its early stages. This is essentially the contention of S. I. Konstorum, for instance. But, though the symptoms of schizophrenia are in a sense functional, their removal requires physiological measures; psychotherapy is useful only to supplement them.

Nevertheless, it is true even an acute form of the disease demands that the physician avail himself of some psychotherapeutic approach to the condition from the very beginning, for this may help considerably to set back the entire growing and broadening symptomatology. It is particularly important to combat the factors which settle down as a "quite superfluous, but otherwise burdensome, load on the weak cortical cells," in the expression of I. P. Pavlov.

Every basic form of psychotherapy is applicable to various states of schizophrenia, though not necessarily with equal success, namely: (1) calming down, explanation, removal of psychogenic symptoms and unnecessary excitement; (2) suggestion and distraction; (3) stimulation of cortical activities; and (4) instruction in adjustment.

The choice of one or another of these techniques

114

of psychotherapy may sometimes be determined experimentally, though we should never forget the fact that, in schizophrenia, positive results sometimes manifest themselves after a considerable delay. In the acute stage of the disease, psychotherapy is advisable for obvious reasons only when the patient's processes of thinking have not been seriously affected. It seems to be theoretically feasible, in general, that the dystrophic processes in the brain may run a more favorable course as long as disturbing stimulation is kept in check.

Psychotherapy is often indicated in the simple form of schizophrenia as well as in the brighter periods of catatonia. It can also be quite successful in the paranoid form, insofar as personality is reasonably well preserved and emotions are not extremely tense. But the technique of persuasion is not particularly effective in these cases, and the patients may resent any interference on the part of the physician with their opinions and habits of conduct. Caution is definitely advisable in these cases.

In the states of abulia and apathy, there may arise an opportunity for psychotherapeutic treatment immediately after the effects of insulin shock make it permissible.

When the patient feels sufficiently well to hope for complete recovery, it is time for the physician to assume the responsibility of guidance. The following three conditions are likely to make psychotherapy successful at this point: (1) clear and helpful relations between the patient and his physician; (2) a modified environment, adjusted to the patient; and (3) stimulation by work and entertainment.

The main purpose of psychotherapy in these cases

lies in moderating autistic, unrealistic thinking, feelings of estrangement or worthlessness, and at the same time in raising psychological tonus. The physician, at this stage of treatment, should avail himself of every suitable opportunity to promote the patient's adjustment. It may be observed, indeed, that a few patients manifest the tendency to regain wholesome motives by themselves; these must be found and developed. Other patients happen to retain knowledge and skills acquired in the school or at work; these must be revived and encouraged. The physician, in trying to stimulate the patient's inclinations to work, to enjoy entertainment, saves him from degradation of inactivity and from pathological personality changes.

# THE USE OF MEDICATION AND PSYCHOTHERAPY IN PSYCHIATRIC CLINICS

by A. S. Poznansky, M. I. Zeitlin,
and I. G. Tokareva
*(Gorki)*

The combination method of treatment, in which pathological symptoms are attacked from several sides simultaneously, sometimes proves to be most effective. Medication and physiotherapy are widely employed together or successively. As to the combination of medication and psychotherapy, it has been used until recently only by a few clinicians, although it has been known for quite a while that the effect of almost every drug and medicinal ingredient depends not only on the properties of the pharmacological agent, but also on the psychological mood of the patient.

The method of combining medication and psychotherapy has been so far considered in psychiatry mainly in the treatment of neuroses and alcoholism. Systematic psychotherapy has been applied to the treatment of psychoses but seldom.

Our own experience with the treatment of neuroses and certain psychoses by means of medication and

117

psychotherapy has demonstrated the existence of various advantages of this method. Hypnotherapy, for instance, was conducted in combination with a number of pharmaceutical preparations. Depending on the nature of the disease and the patient's state of health, we used in some cases soporific drugs, in others insulin, in still others novocaine, etc.

We have observed a marked positive effect of combining hypnotherapy with hypoglycemic doses of insulin in the case of patient C., twenty-five years of age, who developed the so-called parting pains immediately after a surgical operation on stomach ulcer. Earlier treatments, including tissue therapy, brought no relief. The patient had lost almost twenty pounds and remained unemployed for more than one year. But the combination of insulin and hypnosis (twelve sessions) made it possible to discharge him completely healthy within a couple of weeks.

K. M. Bykov and I. T. Kurtsin point out that 'parting' pains are pathological impulsations arising in the ailing tissue or organ and leading to the formation of regional inertness of the cortex. This explains, in the above-mentioned case, the ineffectiveness of the local treatment of the stomach. But the combination of treatments acting on both the cortical and the visceral system could be clearly more effective.

In another case, that of registered nurse K., fifty-four years of age, we observed a typical picture of cancerophobia. Her ailment began after she was sent to have an x-ray picture taken in connection with the stomach aches she had complained of. The roentgenologist asked her several questions, among them "Were there any cases of cancer in your family?" and "Have you any difficulty in swallowing?"

Further examination demonstrated, however, that the patient suffered from nothing but gastritis. Nevertheless, the psychic trauma apparently contributed to a progressive deterioration of the patient's health, with the consequent increase of stomach pains and frequent vomiting. She found it impossible to dismiss the thought of cancer and came to regard her illness incurable; all food was refused and much weight was lost. Insulinotherapy brought no improvement, but the addition of hypnotherapy made it possible to discharge the patient within seven weeks without any trace of physical or mental pathology.

The clinician's attention has been occupied for some time by cases of hypochondria whose etiology and pathogenesis are always exceedingly complex and somewhat uncertain. Our experience has shown, however, that in quite a few instances of hypochondriasis the combination of hypnotherapy with novocaine blockade (to use A. A. Vishnevsky's term) is quite successful. The explanation is really simple: according to available literature, novocaine is a drug helping to normalize interoceptive connections between the internal organs and the cortex (A. A. Vishnevsky, M. V. Kirzon, O. R. Colier, A. M. Zuckerman, Y. G. Kozlov, and others).

Let us examine another case in which the treatment was essentially of the same kind.

Patient B., twenty years of age, entered the Gorki psychoneurological hospital on November 14th, 1952, complaining of recurrent cardiac attacks during which the heart seemed about to stop. During these attacks the patient developed, naturally enough, fear of death and felt, in his own expression, "knocking in the head." The first attack came during a quarrel with a

119

friend, about four months before admission to the hospital. But the examination of the patient, including cardiography, excluded the possibility of an organic heart trouble.

On account of an increasing restlessness of the patient, he had to be transferred to the psychiatric ward. There, after a careful examination, the patient was subjected to hypnotherapy. At the end of the fifth session, he calmed down considerably, but continued to complain. It was then decided to add novocaine blockade to the treatment. As a result of this combination method, the patient's condition noticeably improved and he began rapidly to recover. Altogether there were four blockades and ten hypnotic sessions. The patient was discharged as cured after two months of treatment. According to the record of catamnesis for about four years, he has had no heart attacks and still feels perfectly well.

The mechanism of combination therapy must by no means be interpreted as mere arithmetical summation of the effects of pharmacological preparations and psychotherapeutic action. This has been amply confirmed by medical experience with treatment of several cases of schizophrenia, exemplified by the following one.

Patient K., twenty-five years of age. Diagnosis: schizophrenia. He was suffering from it for about a year. On admission to the hospital he complained of severe headaches; there were hallucinations in the form of "voices" and unpleasant odors. The patient began increasingly to worry about losing his mind. At the same time he became inactive and emotionally indifferent. Insulinotherapy was prescribed to which hypnotherapy was subsequently added. Hypnotic sleep often reached the stage of somnambulism. In that state the patient quite readily responded to suggestion. All posthypnotic suggestions, too, were accepted and, if necessary, promptly enacted. But the hypnotic experiences were invariably affected by amnesia. At the same time, strangely enough, the arterial blood pressure would go down and the pulse would be reduced to fifteen to twenty-five beats per minute.

At the end of the combination treatment consisting altogether of nineteen hypoglycemic states and twelve hypnotic sessions, the patient was discharged sufficiently improved and able to go to work.

All these experimental and clinical data permit us to conclude that the practice of hypnosis in mental disease, notably in schizophrenia, has, in addition to the help it renders, an intimate effect upon the autonomic and metabolic processes.

There are a number of fairly urgent problems, however, which remain to be investigated and possibly solved by persons engaged in research, if the combination method of treatment is to become widely successful. These problems include, above all, the questions of proper selection of words in suggestion and the exact activity of chosen drugs in their total as well as specific effect upon the organism.

# THE RECORD OF PSYCHOTHERAPEUTIC
# WORK IN MENTAL HOSPITALS

## by L. I. Lichtenstein
### *(Moscow)*

Treatment was conducted in a ward for slightly
disturbed women at a hospital in Kazakh U.S.S.R.
There were altogether thirty female patients under
observation. The following method of extended sleep
was used for treatment: all the patients were hypnotized simultaneously at bed time, to sleep for about
eleven to fourteen hours, that is, approximately up to
lunch time. When not under treatment, the patients
were engaged in work of some sort.

The choice of ward patients was determined not
so much by diagnosis as by syndromes of sickness
indicating the presence of protective inhibition; that
is to say, they were exclusively asthenics, astheno-
depressives, or patients suffering from exhaustion after
some active treatment. There was one additional
rule: all violent and disoriented patients were invariably excluded from the group so as to assure conditions of tranquillity, cleanliness, and courteous conduct in the ward. Suitable measures were taken to

promote desire for self-improvement among the patients.

During the waking hours the patients were mainly engaged in reading and conversing; almost every one of them was doing some handwork.

Sleep was induced in the following fashion. A nurse gathered the patients and asked them to lie down in their cots; after that she remained in the ward to attend to various chores and, if necessary, to make observations. In the meantime, the physician started the session of sleep suggestion. The patients were told to fix their eyes on some objects, for instance, an electric bulb. To increase the effect of hypnotic suggestion, some continually monotonous stimuli were utilized.

In the course of time there appeared instances of what may be called a steady "circumstantial reflex." Some patients, when the customary bedtime arrived, would go by themselves to their places, lie down, and fall asleep without any direct suggestion. This circumstantial reflex turned out to be a regular component of the method. The ward was darkened, but only so as to make the patients' faces visible.

Most of the observed patients were almost instantaneously in the light stage of hypnosis, that is, in the state of mere drowsiness. We did not attempt to induce deeper forms of hypnosis. Light sleep caused by general hypnotic suggestion was quite sufficient for the purposes of treatments conducted in absolute silence. For this reason, the location of the ward was of considerable importance, as were also outside silence and a careful selection of patients so that they would not disturb each other and interfere with hypnotic sessions.

Suggestion during sleep was employed only when it was definitely indicated. After a general talk, individual suggestions (spoken in whisper) were used with some of the patients. Toward the end of the second hour the hypnotic sleep usually changed into natural sleep. The patients continued to sleep naturally, though influenced by posthypnotic suggestions, without any interference up to the lunch time, almost invariably retaining their position.

Considering the afternoon rest, the patients' total sleeping time was thus lengthened to twelve to fourteen hours per day. The number of sessions was different for each patient and varied from several to as many as forty or even fifty. On completion of each hypnotic session, a vigorous waking state during the day was generally suggested.

Certain explanatory comments must now be made concerning the nature and effect of our work. After a certain number of sessions of prolonged sleep, our patients manifest desire for activity, and this desire must be encouraged and satisfied. It happens quite often in ordinary mental hospitals that patients remain inactive for months and even years. Our attitude is different: we believe that whenever a patient begins to show signs of recovery, it is of vital importance to organize a plan of activities for him, to give him an opportunity to do something. Work therapy in its broadest sense includes housekeeping, assistance to the hospital personnel, sawing, cultural activities, games, exercise; whatever it be, it can serve as a therapeutic factor supplementing protective treatment. Many of our patients declare that when they work they forget about their troubles and feel much better. Inactive and abulic patients are suggested under hypnosis: "You will put the room in order," "You will saw," or "You are a good worker, don't just sit and do nothing." Thus, almost all of our patients are busy, and by the end of their stay at the hospital they are working quite hard, thus preparing themselves for normal conditions of the outside world.

All this can be illustrated more specifically by the following case history:

Patient N. Diagnosis: schizophrenia. When admitted to the hospital, she was restive, unwilling to eat. She suffered from a delusion of persecution and wanted to go away. At times she was showing signs of waxy flexibility. Thinking that her children were in the adjacent ward (for she heard young voices there), she would enter it and mistake a boy for her son. After insulin therapy she somewhat improved. Delirious utterances became few. But lacking self-confidence, she expressed her reluctance to leave the hospital and said: "If the children can remain here, I shall stay here."

She was then transferred to the ward for sleep therapy. She slept a great deal at first, but improved only slightly. It was consequently suggested to her in sleep that it is important to work and not to be afraid of difficulties of life. Finally, she expressed a desire to join the housekeeping branch. The work was hard there to start with, but she gradually got accustomed to it and felt fine. When discharged from the hospital, she looked well and showed no psychotic symptoms whatsoever.

# PART IV

# TREATMENT OF ALCOHOLISM AND SMOKING

# ON THE ROLE OF SUGGESTION IN THE
# TREATMENT OF ALCOHOLISM

by I. L. Lukomsky
*(Arkhangelsk)*

The question of suggestive therapy as applied to
the treatment of alcoholism is by no means new.
Unfortunately, however, we have failed so far to
attain unanimity in this connection. The results of
investigations published by various authors as to the
effectiveness of available therapeutic methods do not
agree; moreover, there are substantial differences even
with regard to the formulation of the problems to be
solved. These disagreements arise as a result of different theoretical premises and, consequently, of discordant criteria for defining the concept of alcoholism
itself.

Thus S. S. Korsakov and F. E. Rybakov regard
anybody as an alcoholic who manifests symptoms of
organic disturbance caused by frequent consumption
of intoxicating beverages. E. Kraepelin and K. Bonhafer interpret the concept more narrowly, as confined to those who introduce new amounts of alcohol
into the blood before it is completely free from the

previous doses. S. G. Zhislin insists that there is no alcoholism apart from the syndrome of hangover, while I. V. Strielchuk stresses irresistible attraction to alcohol. N. P. Tatarenko, on the other hand, regards attraction to alcohol merely as a secondary phenomenon—a result of extensive organic changes, including those in the higher nervous system and metabolism, themselves caused by repeated consumption of alcohol.

Accordingly, N. P. Tatarenko takes a definite position with regard to the range and succession of research tasks culminating in acceptable treatment. The first thing to do is, in his opinion, to free the organism from all effects of alcohol; second, to raise the tonus of the basic processes in the cortex; third, to remove attraction to alcohol; and fourth, to reinforce the results already attained and to re-educate the patient. In this set-up, methods of psychotherapy (including suggestion) receive a comparatively modest place.

Y. A. Povorinsky interprets the problems of alcoholism in an entirely different way. According to him, the whole process of treatment must be divided into three consecutive stages: protective, reconstructive, and stimulative. Among the most important tasks of the first stage are: to establish an adequate contact with the patient and to apply measures of persuasion aiming to arouse desire for cure in him. The second stage is devoted to speech therapy seeking to produce in the patient a negative attitude toward alcohol, to the reconstruction of his relations with other people, and to the formation of wholesome social attitudes. Of particular importance here is hypnotherapy. The third and last stage consists in stimulation by suggestion and work therapy.

It is our contention that the above-mentioned principles define on the whole correctly the purpose and direction of treatment of alcoholism. But the particular emphasis must be placed on overcoming the original defects of the patient's personality and the resulting attractions of alcohol.

Among the present-day methods of combatting addiction to alcohol most prominent is hypnotherapy made widely known through the work of V. M. Bekhterev. This method owes its success largely to the high suggestibility of the alcoholics to hypnotic suggestion. But the frequency of subsequent return to the addiction makes it imperative to look around for new opportunities both in the improvement of suggestion techniques and in entirely new approaches to the problem of alcoholism itself.

Much publicity has recently been given to the use of sensitizing medications. Some of them have only limited circulation because of their high toxicity. There is one method, however, built around the emetic reaction to alcohol effected by certain drugs, mostly apomorphine, which has been firmly established in psychiatric practice. It has definite possibilities; but, for some reasons, it has been seldom combined with hypnotherapy.

Such disregard cannot be regarded as justified, the more so that the emetic reaction itself is effective only as long as certain principles of psychotherapy are taken into consideration during treatment.

Our experience with the treatment of over three hundred persons suffering from chronic alcoholism—

131

both in the psychiatric clinic of the Arkhangelsk Medical Institute and in the local hospital—demonstrates that certain basic conditions of treatment ought to be invariably fulfilled, insofar as they raise appreciably the effectiveness and permanence of the results attained by suggestive and combination treatment of alcoholism.

The most important condition practically guaranteeing systematic and consequently more effective use of medical measures consists in observing the principles of stages in treatment. Our experience confirms the value of the above-mentioned division (by Y. A. Povorinsky) of treatment of alcoholism into three stages. The central problem of the first stage lies in removing the symptoms which, subjectively, impose serious hardships on the patient: disturbance of sleep and appetite, fluctuation of moods, loss of strength, etc.

Administration of a correct combination of sedatives and tonics goes a long way to win the patient's confidence and to establish in him the belief in the ultimate success of the treatment. All this serves as extremely valuable preparation for the following suggestion therapy.

Suggestion therapy plays a vital role in the second stage of treatment; its principal purpose is to weaken pathological patterns of the patient's personality and conduct and to establish new and wholesome patterns. Hypnotherapy is particularly useful in overcoming the patient's longing for alcohol.

One of the most important conditions of effective hypnotherapy among alcoholics consists in its differential application. In other words, it is necessary to take into consideration not only the clinical picture of the case of addiction, but also its original causes. Some patients turn to alcohol in deceptive hope of raising their efficiency in work or human relations; other patients attempt to narcotize pains or to dull some particularly unhappy experiences; some begin drinking under the influence of their social set; etc.

Equally varied are the impulses compelling alcoholics to seek medical help. Some patients are eager to restore their social status or reputation; other patients want to realize their much postponed plans of life; still others become worried about their failing health; and there are also those who hope to improve disrupted family relations.

Each one of such various yet unique causes of alcoholism as well as of desire to be cured must be taken into consideration as an element of psychotherapy; and this can be done only on the condition of a strictly individualized approach to the case. As a result, in spite of certain advantages of group hypnotic sessions—including higher suggestibility and imitativeness—some limits must be imposed on such sessions in order to avoid excessive standardization tending to lower the effectiveness of this treatment; for the so-called uniform groups of specially selected patients are never really uniform. Consequently, individual sessions are definitely to be preferred, even though they lead to considerable increase in the total amount of work. But even so there is danger of a standardized approach to the patients.

On the whole, a preliminary careful study of the patient may not be avoided. This means that much attention should be given to his medical and general anamnesis. This means also that a somewhat different variation of hypnotherapy must be applied to each patient. To attain such individualized approach to therapy, it becomes necessary to combine clinical examination with a preliminary talk with every patient; and such a talk provides valuable orientation for the patient as well as for his physician. This talk aims, first of all, to explain to the patient the essence of the intended treatment, to dispel his unfounded fears as well as exaggerated expectations, and thus to establish a reasonably correct line of conduct during hypnotherapy. And second, the physician may utilize the talk as an opportunity to determine the degree of the patient's suggestibility, the extent of his information and the composition of his vocabulary. This latter finding is of importance for the choice of verbal forms in hypnotic and posthypnotic suggestion.

In the content of suggestion itself it is advisable to avoid all general schemes and standards; rather, it is preferable to use the very plans which the patient himself builds for his future and thus to make the conquest of alcoholism the main condition for their realization.

In many instances, it is desirable to modify the ways of treatment so as to enhance the effect of psychotherapy. Thus suggestion methods may be combined or alternated with medication or physiotherapy. But every such modification must be reflected also in the content of the posthypnotic suggestion and thus to support the conviction in the patient's mind that the whole course of treatment is conducted in strict agreement with the originally developed plan. Unless this is done, the patient may start suspecting that every new change means that the physician is not quite sure of the success of the chosen treatment.

Among the combination methods of treating alcoholism, quite effective is the use of hypnotherapy together with the formation of a conditioned reflex for vomiting. This method, especially when it avails itself of apomorphine, has unfortunately some counter-indications, among which, according to available literature, are hypotonia, weakness of vessels, brain traumata, etc.

As a result of such counterindications, a new combination method of treating alcoholism has been recently developed: the vomiting reflex is formed without resorting to emetics, namely, by means of suggestion alone. This is done during a hypnotic session by means of weak olfactory and gustatory stimulation accompanied by verbal suggestion.

This and similar combination methods (as devised by E. I. Goldberg, L. M. Dondysh, and I. V. Strielchuk) of treating alcoholism show considerably higher effectiveness than the traditional methods.

The main task of the third stage of treatment consists in consolidating whatever wholesome attitudes have been established in the preceding stage. This is done in most cases outside the hospital. The main difficulty in this connection is found in protectting the patient from the influence of the very persons in his environment who once unwittingly contributed to the development of alcoholism in his case. The struggle with such unhappy influences must be entrusted to the patient's relatives and to his community.

# UNIQUE FACTORS IN THE HYPNOTIC TREATMENT OF CHRONIC ALCOHOLISM

by T. N. Gordova and N. K. Kovalev
*(Kursk)*

The use of apomorphine to establish the vomiting reflex in response to consumption of alcohol has become quite widespread in the treatment of alcoholism. In combination with hypnosis, it produces excellent results, according to I. V. Strielchuk and V. E. Rozhnov. There is one noteworthy objection to the drug, however. In the cardiac and vascular ailments, stomach ulcers, and liver diseases it is definitely counterindicated. But it so happens that alcoholics are exceptionally often affected with these troubles; there arises, consequently, a serious difficulty for the physicians in the choice of treatment for such patients.

This was the reason for our decision to investigate the possibility of developing a suitable methodology of hypnotic treatment for these cases. We had 150 patients under our observation, all chronic alcoholics. Twenty-eight of them were treated by means of hypnosis; in sixty-two cases the combination of hypnosis and apomorphine was used; and sixty patients had only apomorphine. In the first of these groups the use of apomorphine was definitely counter-indicated, because they suffered from hypertonia (12), ulcers or gastritis (8), and heart ailments (8). About half the patients (seventy-two) were between thirty-one and forty years of age.

The distribution of ages at which the abuse of alcohol began, however, presents an entirely different picture. The following table makes it clear:

| Age | Number |
|---|---|
| 20 or less | 3 |
| 21-30 | 114 |
| 31-40 | 24 |
| 41 or more | 3 |

These figures indicate the obvious importance of education in hygiene and prophylactic measures among the adolescents and young people.

The hypnotic sessions were conducted in groups of four or five persons, twice a week for thirty minutes; altogether there were from five to twelve such sessions. There were individual talks before each treatment, during which the effect of alcohol upon the human organism was explained and detailed instructions given with regard to conduct during the coming session. The sessions themselves were conducted in a special room ("hypnotarium"), slightly darkened. The methodology of hypnosis consisted in verbal suggestion of sleep, accompanied with stimulation by rhythmic sounds (clock ticking).

When the patients were all under hypnosis, it was suggested that the sight, smell and taste of alcohol will cause nausea and vomiting. After two or

three sessions each patient received specific suggestions to have hallucinatory experiences connected with
episodes of drinking resulting in feelings of disgust
toward anything containing alcohol. For instance, a
patient would be told that he was in a bar with
a glass of vodka in front of him; and that the taste
and smell of it made him vomit. During this suggestion the patient's face would plainly express disgust,
and initial vomiting movements would be observed.
This effect was particularly well achieved in the
somnambulistic stage of hypnosis. When the intended
result was not observed, the suggestion was supported
by a wad of vodka-soaked cotton placed in front of
the patient's nose. During the next session, vomiting
was observed at mere mention of passing near a bar.

The treatment with apomorphine (sixty-two
patients) began with a minimal dosage which was
gradually increased until the vomiting reaction was
produced. Later on the doses had to be somewhat
increased, for there is a certain tendency to become
habituated to the drug.

Suggestion enabled us to effect the vomiting reflex
also with smaller doses of apomorphine. The patient
was told under hypnosis that each new injection of
apomorphine would cause stronger vomiting, though
the dosage remained the same. Particularly good results of this kind were obtained from the patients
readily reaching the somnambulistic stage.

The effect of this treatment was subsequently
verified through catamnesis among 110 patients. It
showed that hypnotherapy (with or without apomorphine) was more successful than the treatment rely-
ing on apomorphine alone. This is clearly indicated
in the following table:

|  | | Subsequent Abstention | | | |
| Method of Treatment | Number | 3 mo. or less | 3-12 mo. | Year or more | Recent cases |
|---|---|---|---|---|---|
| Hypnotherapy | 23 | 6 | 3 | 11 | 3 |
| Hypnotherapy and apomorphine | 47 | 13 | 7 | 20 | 7 |
| Conditioning with apomorphine | 40 | 20 | 13 | 7 | — |
| Total | 110 | 39 | 23 | 38 | 10 |

The effectiveness of treatment depends on the number of hypnotic sessions. According to our data, we are in a position to recommend no fewer than nine to twelve sessions for a course of treatment of chronic alcoholism.

It may be interesting to note that, when the patients are classified by age, it is observed that the younger people show on the average a more lasting effect of treatment; but then it will be well to remember that the same group was also exposed to fewer years of alcoholism.

### CONCLUSIONS:

1. Comparison of data obtained in three different types of treatment of alcoholism shows that the most desirable effect is reached by means of hypnotherapy, by itself or in combination with apomorphine.

2. Consequently, hypnotherapy as the leading method of treating patients suffering from chronic alcoholism, should be more widely employed.

3. The best results of hypnotherapy are secured by the method in which verbal suggestion of disgust toward alcohol is combined with suggestion of hallucinatory experiences of drinking alcoholic beverages.

4. The therapeutic effect, in cases of alcoholism, is increased in proportion to the depth of the hypnotic state attained, from which follows the advantage of inducing, whenever possible, the somnambulistic state.

5. In the treatment of persons afflicted with chronic alcoholism, the degree of hypnotizability should be taken into consideration, for the highly hypnotizable persons can be treated without resorting to the injection of apomorphine, especially when there are counterindications to it.

6. In dealing with patients insufficiently susceptible to hypnosis, it may be wise to combine its use with that of apomorphine; and suggestion should itself be then directed toward the increase of vomiting reactions and, consequently, to decreasing the amount of required apomorphine.

7. When dealing with persons difficult to hypnotize, it is advisable to precede the treatment with an explanatory talk.

8. It is recommended that an average course of hypnotic treatment consist of nine to twelve sessions. In alcoholism of long duration, it may be necessary to extend the number of sessions up to fifteen.

# A STUDY OF SELECTIVE RAPPORT
# IN HYPNOSIS

by I. O. Narbutovich
*(Stalingrad)*

The study of clinical phenomena and physiological mechanisms of hypnosis, as an important method of psychotherapy, has both theoretical and practical significance. Much attention has already been devoted to the problems connected with it in this country and elsewhere.

One of the peculiarities of hypnotic sleep lies in the existence of rapport or, to use I. P. Pavlov's expression, of the guarding point.

It is generally believed that rapport is strictly selective, that it is limited to the hypnotizing person alone, and that, to transfer rapport to somebody else, it is necessary to utter a special suggestion to this effect. To verify this contention we conducted an experiment with eleven men and two women, all suffering from chronic alcoholism.

Our findings show that full selectivity does not exist even in the somnambulistic stage of hypnosis, when inhibition is at its highest. These findings are in complete accord with those of V. E. Rozhnov.

There arises therefore the question as to the reasons for the above-mentioned belief concerning the strict selectivity of rapport in hypnosis. Our observations demonstrate that such selectivity is by no means automatic; rather, it is artificially induced by means of a special suggestion amounting to direct or indirect instruction to disregard the voice of any person except the hypnotist himself. The latter may declare: "You do not hear anything but my voice; you listen to no one but myself." Or else it may amount to the simple order: "From now on you will hear only my voice."

It must be added in this connection that the hypnotized person is likely to be sensitive to suggestions of any degree or shade. Here is a good illustration of this:

Patient P., thirty-seven years of age; suffers from chronic alcoholism. The physician conducting the hypnotic session lifts the patient's left arm and utters the following suggestion: "Your arm will remain in this position until I make it free." At that moment another physician says: "I shall count one, two, three, and at the count 'three' the muscles of your left arm will relax and it will drop." He then counts, but the arm does not drop. After this the physician-hypnotist continues with the therapeutic suggestions, at the conclusion of which he lifts the patient's right arm and suggests "Your arm will remain in this position until it is freed." Whereupon the other physician repeats his former remarks. At the count of 'three' the arm drops.

This example demonstrates that if the hypnotist would use in the first suggestion the phrase "until it is freed" instead of "until I make it free," the result of interference by another person might be quite

142

different. For there was no response to the first remark of his, whereas the second remark called forth a positive action.

Similar results were obtained with other subjects, all testifying to the absence of any automatic and strict rapport.

### CONCLUSIONS:

1. Selectivity of hypnotic rapport depends as a rule on special suggestion. To make the rapport selective, it suffices that the hypnotist say, "You will hear only my voice." In instances when such suggestion is not given, the selective rapport is likely to be limited or completely absent.

2. The hypnotized person often responds to the minutest shades of suggestion. This means that all suggestions ought to be carefully prepared and precisely worded.

# PSYCHOTHERAPY OF SMOKING

## by Y. A. Povorinsky
### *(Leningrad)*

The problem of how to combat the addiction to smoking deserves serious consideration. People who do not smoke cannot understand the psychology of smokers. And the men and women who have succeeded in overcoming the habit by themselves do not quite appreciate the typical smoker's need for help. Nevertheless, the problem is by no means simple. It is not easy, indeed, to quit smoking. There are many people who, though knowing full well the obvious harm of smoking and eager to abandon the persistent habit, simply cannot do it without outside help.

I. V. Strielchuk notes correctly that treatment of smoking is one of the most difficult tasks in the field of narcomania. When smokers are deprived of tobacco, they may manifest the attitude comparable to that of an abstaining morphinist. The reaction to abstaining from tobacco is somewhat different, to be sure: to some it is quite easy, to others very difficult.

The smoking of tobacco is the most widespread form of narcomania. In spite of the fact that smoking is harmful and must be forbidden in some illnesses, literature on its treatment is so far scarce.

I. V. Strielchuk is in favor of medicinal therapy, but he also points out that psychotherapy plays an important role in the treatment of smokers; he remarks, moreover, that psychotherapy, when used systematically, may be of considerable benefit. A. M. Rapoport advocates the use of pilocarpine in the treatment of smokers. At a conference of the Moscow Narcotic Society some time ago (in 1925), it was pointed out that individual treatment of smokers is wasteful of time and contrary to good sense; accordingly a motion was passed to abandon such treatment. Instead of it, group therapy was recommended.

We do not deny the prophylactic significance of the group method; at the same time, we feel that individual psychotherapy is the only acceptable method whenever a well-established habit must be overcome. Smoking is an easily acquired addiction and, consequently, it is usually associated with all kinds of phenomena of everyday life. My own experience with a large number of cured smokers seems to indicate that a more conscientious and careful selection of the therapeutic measures is indicated in each case.

Let me enumerate the principal methods of treating smokers in contemporary medicine:

1. *Treatment with medication.* This includes gargling and smearing of the inner surface of the mouth with a weak solution of *argenti nitrici* or protargol, which causes a presumably unpleasant taste during smoking. Addition of *radix Heleniae* to tobacco also results in objectionable sensations. This method is

rarely successful, according to our obervations, because it usually leads to plain resentment or even to deception.

2. *Treatment with hypnosis* involving prohibition to smoke. Beginning with the first visit by the patient, it is suggested during hypnosis that the taste of cigarettes is disgusting to him, that he does not wish to smoke at all, etc. The effect of this method cannot be called very satisfactory, for the suggestion disregards many experiences intimately connected with smoking; it has been known to establish various complex conflicts within the patient's mind.

Two episodes will suffice to illustrate the problem. A physician made a suggestion to his patient, a woman, that cigarette smoking will produce vomiting; but he did not think of mentioning the loss of desire to smoke. As a result, she felt exceedingly uncomfortable, for every attempt to smoke led to vomiting. Finally she returned to the doctor demanding that the suggestion be revoked, since in the meantime she had lost all desire to abandon smoking.

Another patient was given the suggestion to be physically unable to smoke at all. This case also ended in failure. When he came home, he was indeed unable to smoke, though desire to do so was very strong. Several hours later, he became extremely irritable and excited. Late in the evening he called his physician by telephone asking for help. When permission was granted, he asserted he was still unable to smoke, even though a pack of cigarettes was lying in front of him. This patient eventually resumed smoking, too, and refused to abandon the habit.

3. *Treatment by persuasion.* This method offers a possibility of emotional influence upon the smoker;

but its results are accidental by nature, for persuasion to be truly effective must take the patient's personality into consideration. Most smokers planning to quit know full well of the harmfulness of smoking, but find it impossible to end the habit. In other words, they are already persuaded but weak.

All the above-mentioned methods are sometimes combined in a variety of ways and may bring about favorable results. But their theoretical foundation is inadequate and it is difficult, therefore, to explain why in some cases the results are good, while in other cases the treatment fails completely or succeeds only temporarily.

Case studies of both successful and unsuccessful treatments of smokers permit us to identify the elements of the situation, to generalize our observations, and to attempt finding the theoretical foundation of the method we can call correct, because it explains the problem and helps the patients overcome their addiction.

It is necessary to distinguish among several stages of the kind of treatment we propose. The first stage consists in the examination of the smoker's personality, the compelling reasons for turning to smoking as well as for wishing to quit smoking. The second stage amounts to the registration of all the relevant and significant facts, sensations, and experiences during smoking or during abstention from smoking. The third stage, following an exhaustive study of the individual, is devoted to treatment under hypnosis.

In interviewing a smoker, it is important to collect, in addition to routine data, information in reply to the following questions: (1) How long has the patient been smoking? (2) Under what circumstances did he begin to smoke? (3) Did he ever try to quit smoking? (4) What has aroused his present desire to quit smoking? (5) On what occasions does he particularly want to smoke? (6) What attitude does he manifest in smoking? Does he pay any attention to his sensations or does he smoke mechanically as it were? (7) How many cigarettes on the average does he smoke per day?

Such an interview dwells particularly on the data which will be of particular significance during treatment. It should not, however, merely collect the relevant data. Among its many purposes are also understanding of the patient's personality and the development of an attitude of mutual trust between the patient and the physician. The former should have every opportunity to express himself, for even the most insignificant details might prove to be of considerable value in the subsequent treatment. In these cases, just as in any case of neurosis, it is desirable to conduct an unhurried conversation through which the physician familiarizes himself with the patient's personality, social connections, and the circumstances of his life during its entire duration up to the moment.

Most important are, of course, the ideas the smoker has about his own smoking—its causes, satisfactions, annoyances, and especially the worries making him seek the physician's help. As far as the success of treatment and prognosis are concerned, much depends on the clarification of the patient's desire to stop smoking. If the conflict underlying it can be resolved, the chance of success is greatly increased; otherwise, the outcome is doubtful.

The complexity of the problem becomes clear when we consider the following case.

Patient K., a woman, has been smoking for a long time. But recently she was informed that she suffered from tuberculosis of the lungs. The motive to quit smoking seems to be obvious: she wants to get well. But actually the harm of smoking does not worry her very much. The talk reveals that the patient is engaged to be married to a man who does not smoke. Naturally enough, she is thinking about her relations with the future husband. She is worrying about such things as tobacco smell from her mouth, color of skin, and the like. When the true reason for the desire to quit smoking becomes clear, the success of treatment becomes almost assured.

Strong motivation is of considerable help, of course, in re-conditioning the patient's attitude toward smoking. We remember a case where a smoker was cured from his habit almost instantaneously. He developed an acute catarrh of the throat and came to consult a laryngologist who, after examining him, declared that, unless he quit smoking, he was bound to develop tuberculosis of the throat. The patient formed his decision to stop smoking right there and never smoked again.

Unfortunately, however, the great majority of patients approaching a physician with request for help in this connection are by no means easy cases. There are too many links in the chain of their desires and hesitations, hopes and doubts, fears and worries to see the situation clearly, to evaluate it correctly, and to state it precisely. As a result, they are seldom able to inform the physician as to the exact cause of their difficulties. We often deal here with hidden,

149

introvertive motives or, to use A. G. Ivanov-Smolensky's expression, with the pathodynamic structure of human personality. The patient's belief that he ought to quit smoking remains cold as it were as long as it is abstracted from the mass of confused emotions. The best that a physician can do in such cases is to encourage the smoker's vague "scruples" and dissatisfactions with himself.

After a careful examination of the patient's life experiences and attitudes, we must turn to the second stage of treatment, which may be called "registration" of detailed facts in experimental changes in the patient's habit of smoking. This should by no means be done in a mechanical manner. When the patient is instructed to cut down the number of cigarettes per day, he is bound to think of the next cigarette and, in addition to suffer from the effort he is making. This is likely to end very simply: the patient returns to his old habit of smoking.

When a physician, in his conversation with the patients, turns to the question of regulating smoking, and the patients learn what is expected of them, a high percentage refuse at once to follow the instruction. Even among the smokers expressing willingness to regulate the extent of their smoking, there are many who would not obey the physician's orders. Some who would, might be negligent about recording the exact number of cigarettes they smoke.

To regulate the smoking more efficiently, the patient is asked, to start with, not to smoke for one whole day; or, if this is beyond his power, for as long as he can. During this period he must direct all his attention toward the sensations resulting from abstention. The next day, however, he is permitted to smoke as much as he pleases and without any restraint; but then he must record every single cigarette, the exact time, the occasion, and the detailed experiences he is able to notice. After that, regulation of smoking demands, in addition to proper recording, reduction in the number of smoked cigarettes, in accordance with the physician's plan. The patient is told, moreover, not to smoke before and after eating, and at night; and he must never smoke more than one cigarette at a time.

The difficulty characterizing the therapy of smoking, as compared to the therapy of other forms of narcomania, consists mainly in this, that the process of smoking has numerous well-established ties of conditioning. Smoking is, in fact, the easiest form of narcomania, least limited by place, time, income, and other conditions. That is why fight against automatisms of smoking, against various habitual associations is so significant in the treatment of the habit. When the patient consents to recording every cigarette he smokes, his attention is directed to activities previously performed almost unconsciously. The strength of automatisms is thus sapped, undermined.

The fact is, as our records clearly show, that the best results are obtained among the patients who follow the physician's instructions accurately and meticulously.

It would not be right completely to disregard the physiological changes accompanying abstention from smoking. Their existence has been denied by A. G. Stoyko, but the majority of investigators, among them A. M. Rapoport, D. M. Lachman, and I. V. Strielchuk, attribute considerable importance to them.

These changes include rise in irritability, lowering

of working ability, and other effects of disturbance in the habitual balance of bodily activities. Experiments with animals demonstrate that nicotine introduced into their organism serves first as a stimulant and later as a depressant of the nervous system. But it must be conceded that the physiological effects of abstention among human beings differ in intensity from person to person.

Hypnotic suggestion itself, which culminates the progress of treatment, is not necessarily the most important part of it. We turn to it only when the patient has been thoroughly prepared for it. Putting the patient into the hypnotic state aims only at creating the most favorable conditions for consolidating the results of treatment. And the state of hypnosis is undoubtedly the best state in which to receive suggestion. We do not seek, however, deep sleep for suggestion. Experience shows, as a matter of fact, that suggestion as well as persuasion, analysis as well as synthesis of ideas are more efficient in the lighter forms of hypnosis than in the deeper ones, with amnesia that often follows them.

In most instances, cessation of smoking takes place after the first session. But it is always desirable to have another session the following day and again two days later. It happens occasionally that the patient returns to smoking, usually after some unpleasant experience, when self-control has been weakened. But such failures are easily corrected.

# PART V

PSYCHOTHERAPY IN SOMATIC AILMENTS

# USE OF HYPNOTHERAPY IN CASES OF
## BRONCHIAL ASTHMA

### by I. I. Bull
### *(Leningrad)*

The study of etiology and pathogenesis of bronchial asthma began in Russia about a century ago. In
1863, A. Rodossky, in his doctoral dissertation, wrote
that at the root of this disease lies neurosis of the central nervous system. He contended that each attack of
asthma is largely caused by unhappy experiences and
negative emotions.

This idea was further developed in the works of
S. P. Botkin, N. F. Golubov, and others. The material
collected in the studies of the activities of the nervous
system, both normal and pathological, by Russian
physiologists, including I. M. Sechenov, I. P. Pavlov,
N. E. Vvedensky, A. A. Ukhtomsky, made it possible
to develop the contemporary theory of bronchial
asthma and to find the path along which the treatment
of this complex ailment must follow from now on.

In continuing the work of their predecessors, a
few Soviet clinical scholars, notably M. Y. Aryev, L. L.
Vassilyev, Y. P. Frolov, M. V. Chernorutzky, and

others, developed and enriched our understanding of bronchial asthma and thus established the corticovisceral theory of its etiology and pathogenesis.

There are now several hypotheses attempting to explain the mechanism of asthmatic attacks. One of them claims that the main factor lies in the spasm of the smooth muscles of the bronchia; another attributes it to the increased secretion of mucus; the third finds it in the enlargement of vessels and the mucus membrane of the bronchi. In our own interpretation, all these facts are true, but the main factor is indeed the bronchial spasm.

It is our belief that the use of hypnosis will greatly facilitate the study of the problem.

Scientific literature contains a few references to the use of hypnosis in cases of bronchial asthma, namely, by O. Wetterstrand, V. M. Belous, A. Marx, D. A. Vigdorovich, A. N. Bernstein, and V. E. Rozhnov. All these authors treated bronchial asthma with hypnosis and obtained good results.

We observed one hundred such cases between 1951 and 1955 in the Leningrad Medical Institute of I. P. Pavlov. All the patients underwent a course of hypnotherapy and were under observation from two to three years after that. There were altogether seventy-eight women and twenty-two men. By age their distribution was as follows:

| | | | |
|---|---|---|---|
| 10 - 20 years | 2 | 41 - 50 years | 15 |
| 21 - 30 " | 14 | 51 - 60 " | 48 |
| 31 - 40 " | 21 | | |

According to the duration of the disease, the cases were distributed as follows:

| Less than a year | 3 | 21 - 30 years | 10 |
|---|---|---|---|
| 1 - 10 years | 53 | 31 - 40 " | 5 |
| 11 - 20 " | 29 | | |

The patients were divided into three groups, according to the gravity of the ailment, frequency of the attacks, and heart and lungs complications. Those with a few attacks per years and without complications (8) were classified as light cases.

The patients with several attacks per month (56), who also suffered from the initial form of chronic emphysema of the lungs, comprised the second group.

The patients with several attacks per day (36), with both lung and heart complications in most cases, formed the third group.

In ninety cases the disease was preceded by infection of the organs of breathing—pneumonia, grippe, chronic bronchitis, etc. In fifty-one cases the first attack of asthma followed an aggravation of the infection. In forty-nine cases the decisive factor consisted in psychological traumatic experience or lasting negative emotions.

Among the patients there were some who, in addition to asthma, suffered from other diseases as well. Five had hypertonia; three, gastric ulcers; five, chronic cholicystitis. Fifty patients were known to suffer from neuroses (twenty-four, from neurasthenia; sixteen, from psychasthenia; and ten, from hysteria). All diagnoses were made by specialists.

In the course of treatment certain indications in favor of hypnotherapy were found, among them:

1. Absence of acute infections in the organs of breathing.

2. Sufficient suggestibility of the patient or his desire to be treated by hypnosis.

3. Connection of asthmatic attacks with some mental trauma or negative emotions.

4. Presence of obvious mechanisms of conditioned reflexes in connection with recurrent attacks (depending on smells, time of the day or night, specific environment, etc.).

5. Coincidental diagnosis of mental ailments, namely, neurasthenia, psychasthenia, hysteria.

Individual sessions of hypnotherapy continued for about thirty minutes, every second day. The whole course of treatment consisted of ten to thirty sessions, depending on the need. Thirty patients were hypnotized at first individually and then, with their consent, they formed a group.

Hypnosis was conducted by means of verbal suggestion of somnolescence and strengthened, depending on individual requirements, by visual, auditory or tactile stimulation.

Three degrees of the depth of hypnosis were distinguished: light, medium and deep. The first was typical of fifteen patients; the second, of forty-eight; the third, of twenty-seven. And ten persons could not be hypnotized at all.

The therapeutic suggestions were, on the whole, organized on the basis of the patients' complaints and the progress of health conditions. We tried to keep up their morale and improve their disposition. In cases of insomnia, it was suggested to sleep well and soundly, as before illness. All the possible effects of weather change and odors upon the attacks as also of worries and other emotional disturbances were counteracted by special suggestions. During the treatments patients' attention was directed toward the facility of their breathing which, in general, tends to become normal under hypnosis. Throughout the sessions the pulse and blood pressure were taken from time to time. As a rule, the pulse was slower by five to ten beats per minute, while blood pressure was slightly higher.

The following findings should be mentioned:

1. Forty-two patients (out of 100) had steady and lasting remission. Nine of them had no asthmatic attacks for two or three years thereafter; six for a year and a half; twenty-seven, for no less than six months.

2. Twenty-eight patients showed definite improvement. Fifteen of them manifested occasional but rare attacks, which did not prevent them from returning to work. Thirteen had attacks from time to time, but could not go to work.

3. Thirty patients were apparently not affected by hypnotherapy. It is necessary to point out, however, that ten of them could not be properly hypnotized, while the other twenty never reached a sufficiently deep state.

CONCLUSIONS:

1. Hypnotherapy is both physiologically and pathogenically a sound method of treating asthmatic patients. The treatment is particularly indicated in cases where the usual medication brings no relief.

2. The patients suffering from bronchial asthma manifest, under the influence of hypnosis, positive

changes in many organic functions: breathing improves, the lung capacity increases, the arterial pressure rises.

3. Treatment by hypnosis has been statistically justified. Forty-two patients (out of 100) showed much improvement and had no attacks for the duration of six months to three years. Twenty-eight patients were well improved; the attacks were conspicuously milder and rarer. The rest showed no significant change.

# PSYCHOTHERAPY IN
# PSYCHOGENIC THYREOTOXICOSIS

## by M. Kashpur
### (Kharkov)

The present report deals with speech therapy applied to thyreotoxicoses, used whenever there are psychogenic factors in the case history.

There is nothing new in the belief that this disease may be caused by psychological trauma. There is much evidence to the effect that symptoms of this disease may appear as a result of some functional disturbance of the activities of the thyroid gland unbalanced by negative experiences in the patient's life. A number of authors referred to this in the past. S. P. Botkin wrote that symptoms of thyreotoxicosis may appear within hours after a strong emotional experience. Dubois, in his time, remarked that "in some instances Basedow's disease arises in an acute form as a result of a strong moral shock."

Recently published material shows that psychogenic sources of this illness are quite common. Thus Andres and Vilkomirsky point out that thirty-five percent of 228 cases of thyreotoxicosis they treated were psychogenic in origin. More recently (1952), M. A. Kopelovich and N. M. Draznin compiled material on 547 cases of this illness, of which 53.6% were found to be psychogenic in origin.

It has been known for some time already that the treatment of Basedow's disease by means of psychotherapy is likely to bring about positive results. We ourselves had an opportunity to observe seventy-five cases with Basedow's syndrome. One group consisted of people who had suffered from the ailment for a long time (from seven to twelve years); the other was composed of comparatively recent cases (from one to two years). In forty-eight cases the disease was clearly psychogenic in origin. Every one of them had typical symptoms of thyreotoxicosis, such as protrusion of the eyeballs, high rate of metabolism, enlargement of the thyroid, tachycardia. Everyone of them complained of palpitation of the heart, trembling of fingers, excessive perspiration, diarrhea, loss of weight, insomnia, feelings of weakness. We were able to observe high excitability as well as low spirits. Some of the patients reported persistent fears and psychogenic hallucinations.

Twenty-two of these patients were subjected to speech therapy with positive results in each instance. A few case histories will illustrate the problem, treatment and outcome.

1. Patient A., twenty-two years of age. Developed sickness after a fright caused by an attempt by a neighbor to rape her. From that time on she manifested neurotic symptoms. Within several weeks, there appeared enlargement of the neck, heart palpitations, frequent panting. She was forced to abandon her

school studies for six months. Anti-thyroid treatment brought no improvement; in fact, her condition became worse.

Next she had four sessions of psychotherapy, both in the waking and hypnotic state. After the first session there was a marked improvement. Her worries disappeared and she was able to go to work. A month later the patient came back for a check-up. All the former symptoms either vanished or considerably decreased. She was permitted to resume her studies.

2. Patient I., thirty-two years of age. For three years she worried a great deal about her little children's various illnesses and spent many a sleepless night. The family situation was further complicated by the husband's alcoholism. During the fourth year the patient lost all of her three children. As a result, she developed various neurotic symptoms aggravated by thyreotoxicosis.

Six sessions of psychotherapy brought about marked improvement of her condition and she was discharged from the hospital. For four years she felt fine. But death of her mother brought the old symptoms back. This time psychotherapy was conducted exclusively by correspondence, in which she was reminded of her earlier treatments. Soon the patient felt much better, was able to sleep; the trembling of fingers disappeared. There was no more tachycardia or diarrhea.

3. Patient F., thirty years of age. Symptoms of thyreotoxicosis, including exophthalmia, high pulse, perspiration, trembling of fingers, loss of weight, excitability, insomnia. Three years before, her father had been killed by a railroad train right before her

eyes. At that time she developed progressive Basedow's disease and was finally operated on for goiter. But recently she had had the misfortune of losing her only child and had developed the above-mentioned symptoms.

This time the patient was subjected to psychotherapy with deep sleep (eight sessions). She recovered, gained in weight and was able to go to work.

Our interpretation of the Basedow's syndrome as a local psychogenic disturbance of the regulatory work of the cortex is based on the doctrines of I. P. Pavlov and the experimental work by K. M. Bykov.

In all our treatments we use speech therapy. After investigating the causes and conditions of the patient's sickness, we begin with explanatory and calming suggestions in the waking state. This is followed by hypnotic sleep. The patient remains asleep for two hours each time and is given suggestions of deep rest and restoration of strength. Additional suggestions are determined by the patient's case history and symptoms.

There are altogether from four to ten such sessions, depending on the patient's condition and the rate of improvement.

# THE SIGNIFICANCE OF PSYCHOTHERAPY IN OBSTETRICS AND GYNECOLOGY

by V. I. Zdravomyslov
*(Stavropol)*

In obstetrics, the role of 'word' as an anaesthetic factor is extremely great.

Childbirth is the only physiological act which as a rule takes place painfully, even though all the tissues of the organism have been prepared for the event (by slowly becoming more elastic) during nine months.

The pains of childbirth are of two kinds: natural and suggested. The suggested pains develop as a result of widespread conviction that they are inevitable. This conviction has been cultivated from generation to generation and affirmed and reaffirmed by relatives and friends, and also by religious circles, medicine and literature. And this suggested aspect of birth pains is by far the more significant.

The marked increase of the cortical "threshold of sensitivity" to the impulses of pain during childbirth can be considerably lowered, however; sometimes it can be completely overcome. But even more can be done by 'mere words' to remove suggested pains. In fact, no other known method offers better results than anaesthesia of childbirth by means of suggestion.

We are able to report on the results of suggested painless birth in one thousand cases. Seven hundred of them had prophylactic preparation while three hundred underwent suggestion of painlessness only during the process of childbirth. In eighty percent of all cases there was marked positive effect, and in forty percent there was no pain whatsoever.

Counterindications to childbirth anaesthesia by medication are practically synonymous with the entire so-called "obstetrical pathology." It includes diseases of the heart, liver, kidneys, and other organs. But suggestive anaesthesia has no counterindications at all.

It is permitted to use suggestion for painless birth during delivery ("therapy of pain") and in preparation for it ("prophylaxis of childbirth pains").

It is very important to give women thorough acquaintance with the physiology and processes of birth as well as with the activities at any moment of birth labors. Suggestive preparation should preferably begin early during consultations. This can be followed by suggestions of painless birth. During these sessions all negative emotions connected with pregnancy and childbirth should be removed and replaced by positive emotions. And incidentally, additional suggestions may be given with regard to proper sleep, bowel movements, moods, etc. On the average, a woman needs up to six sessions, though the sufficient effect may be attained even in one.

These suggestions can be conducted individually or collectively. For the latter purpose groups of thirty or thirty-five women are indicated. The cases of first pregnancy react on the whole better to suggestion than others.

Suggestion works particularly well in the presence of the psychotherapist at the time of childbirth. He may prefer the woman to be in a waking state, so that she could know what happens and to cooperate with the processes of birth. But it cannot be denied that the best results are still obtained in deep hypnotic sleep.

The following table shows the results of psychotherapy on the painlessness of childbirth in its statistical correlation with the depth of suggestion.

| Depth of suggestion during childbirth | No. of cases | Effect on painlessness of birth | | |
|---|---|---|---|---|
| | | Complete | Fair | No effect |
| Waking state in the absence of the psychotherapist. | 641 | 175 (27.3%) | 304 (47.4%) | 162 (25.2%) |
| Waking state in his presence. | 246 | 138 (56.2%) | 90 (36.5%) | 18 (7.3%) |
| Light hypnosis. | 83 | 67 (80.8%) | 15 (18.0%) | 1 (1.2%) |
| Deep hypnosis. | 30 | 28 (93.3%) | 2 (6.7%) | 0 (0.0%) |
| Total | 1000 | 408 (40.8%) | 411 (41.1%) | 181 (18.1%) |

# PSYCHOTHERAPY OF HYPOGALACTIA OF NURSING MOTHERS

by A. T. Belyaeva, G. I. Vinokurov,
V. I. Zdravomyslov, T. M. Kravchenko,
and N. I. Kuymova
*(Stavropol)*

A complete absence of milk (agalactia) happens
only in acutely pathological changes in the breast
glands, such as their atrophy, inborn abnormality, and
serious injuries to them. In the absence of such
pathological changes, practically every woman has the
ability, at the time of childbirth, to nurse her baby.
U. F. Dombrovskaya observed agalactia only in one
percent of the cases, M. S. Maslov in four percent,
and other authors between two and ten percent. Much
more frequently one finds merely insufficient amount
of milk, or hypogalactia. According to M. S. Maslov,
hypogalactia is found among anywhere between fifteen and twenty-five percent of the nursing mothers.
I. Y. Polyak-Braginskaya observed the phenomenon
in thirty-seven percent.

Unfortunately, hypogalactia compels many mothers to transfer children to artificial feeding too early, sometimes from the very first days of their life. In many instances, this predisposes them to various illnesses connected with disturbances of nutrition. To avoid this, a variety of dietetic, pharmaceutical, and other measures have been devised. But the most efficient approach to the problem, in M. S. Maslov's opinion, lies in psychotherapy.

The first physician to introduce suggestion therapy in this connection was V. I. Zdravomyslov (1935). His findings showed at that time positive results in eighty-nine percent of the cases. Some years later, suggestion therapy was organized, under his leadership, in the First Child Polyclinic in Stavropol to treat hypogalactia and related nutritional difficulties. In addition to hypogalactia and agalactia, psychotherapy was applied also to cases of hypergalactia and defects of the nipples.

There were altogether seventy nursing mothers under observation. The number of sessions varied from one to sixteen, according to need.

Increase in the quantity of milk in the breasts was considered as an objective evidence of success of the treatment. The success was regarded as full when the mother was able, on the conclusion of the therapy, to nurse the baby exclusively by breast, while the baby was gaining in weight. By partial success we understood the situation in which the supply of mother's milk appreciably increased, but insufficiently so to provide the baby with adequate nutrition.

The whole picture of results of this treatment can be seen in the following table:

170

| Type of Dysfunction | Results | of | Psychotherapy | |
| | Full success | Partial success | No success | Number |
| --- | --- | --- | --- | --- |
| Agalactia | 2 | — | 5 | 7 |
| Hypogalactia | 28 | 18 | 14 | 60 |
| Tight nipples | — | 2 | — | 2 |
| Hypergalactia | 1 | — | — | 1 |
| Total | 31 | 20 | 19 | 70 |
| Percentage | 44.3% | 28.6% | 27.1% | 100.0% |

# THE USE OF HYPNOSIS AND
# CONDITIONED-REFLEX THERAPY
# IN DERMATOLOGY

by M. M. Zheltakov
*(Moscow)*


Much research work has been done in our country
and abroad on the application of hypnosis to various
areas of medicine, including that of dermatology.
Most authors refer to the high effectiveness of hypnosuggestive therapy. Nevertheless, this method had so
far a rather limited use in general medical practice
or specifically in dermatology.

But the time has arrived to put the findings
together and to draw proper conclusions from the
total experience of our psychotherapists, and also to
list the indications and counterindications for hypnotic
treatment of various ailments.

We definitely recommend a much wider use of
hypnosuggestive therapy, but insist on the importance
of individualization in both methods of treatment and
the contents of suggestion.

The problem of making hypnotic suggestion individualized, whenever this type of treatment is clearly

172

indicated, is difficult and complex, for it is determined not only by the nature of the disease, but also by the functional state of the patient's nervous system at the time of contraction of sickness and the beginning of treatment. Nor should the type of the higher nervous activity be disregarded.

It happens sometimes that the physician using hypnosis for the purposes of treatment does not consider the patient's personality and what can be done with it under the circumstances. This is likely to result in a lower effectiveness of hypnotherapy and may even discredit the method in the eyes of other physicians and patients.

Hypnosis is no panacea, but only one of the most effective methods of acting upon the patient's organism through the higher centers of his nervous system —his cortex. Physicians of different specializations sometimes vaguely refer to their patients as having some neurotic tendencies. Actually the patient may be suffering from, say, an ulcer or hypertonia, eczema or psoriasis. Should the patient be treated by hypnosis? Definitely so. But it does not follow at all from these considerations that this patient should be treated *only* in this way. He may need *also* other forms of treatment, such as diet or medication. Unless these facts are taken into consideration, the failure of treatment cannot be attributed to hypnosis alone.

It is very important to remember that, in the development of various diseases, the neural and mental traumatic conditions, the overstimulation of the nervous system, and difficult personal experiences may play a tremendous role; such things quite often lead to neuroses. This is particularly true of patients suffering from skin diseases, some of which are difficult to cure, such as eczema, neuro-dermatosis, psoriasis, etc. A neurosis of such patients may have many different causes. On the one hand, the skin disease may contribute to the aggravation of the previously existing neurosis; and on the other, the neurotic condition itself may have originated as a result of a serious and prolonged skin disease. In either case, neurosis is likely to add to the unpleasantness of the situation.

Clinical observations demonstrate that neurotic conditions are significantly common among patients suffering from these diseases. The explanation is simple enough. Many skin ailments, for instance, eczema, neuro-dermatosis, honeycomb tetter, psoriasis, or nettle rash are usually accompanied by itching, sometimes quite intense and persistent. Itching is likely to cause some disturbances in the nervous system, merely because the patients with these troubles are excitable and irritable. They may suffer from insomnia, too, and there may be some consequences of autonomic origin.

It is rather unfortunate that, in skin diseases, the patient has an opportunity almost at all times to observe the manifestations of his disease. Even a slightest deterioration in the picture of his malady affects his psychology and leads to unfavorable developments. This is particularly so when the disease is localized on the open and readily visible portions of the skin, especially on the face or hands; functional disturbances of the nervous system are quite common in these cases. Such disturbances occur even when the trouble happens to be minor, a mere cosmetic defect. Nevertheless, the psychological state of these people may be seriously affected. When in addition, friends and neighbors manifest the attitude of

174

squeamishness and aversion toward what they see, the effect upon the patient's mental mood may be quite bad.

Many patients of this sort really need hypnotic treatment. Appropriate suggestion easily overcomes functional disturbances of the nervous system, helps to instill in the patient's mind confidence in the treatment he receives, and establishes good feelings and a spirit of calmness and security. All this brings about most desirable results in night rest and everything conducive to the improvement of health.

It must be pointed out, however, that in many instances of skin ailment, for example, eczema of a limited spread, there is no conspicuous effect whatsoever upon the nervous system. Nevertheless, even in these cases hypnosuggestive therapy brings about considerable improvements.

Thus we see that in many skin ailments of whatever degree of seriousness the use of hypnosis is clearly indicated. But let us not assume that every skin disease can be cured in this way. Many things can be done by means of hypnosis. In some instances it enables us to remove a neurotic condition and to create a favorable effect upon the course of treatment. In other instances, we are able to attain a complete cure of the patient; in still other instances, the therapy employed with the patient is strengthened by suggestion; and finally some particularly distressing symptoms—pains, itching, insomnia, worries, etc.—are readily overcome and thus enable the treatment to continue under happier conditions.

On the whole, the effectiveness of hypnotherapy in skin diseases depends on many factors, among them:

(1) correct indications for its use;

(2) suitable methodology;

(3) the nature and seriousness of the sickness;

(4) the ability of the physician to employ hypnotherapy with skill; and

(5) the patient himself, the type of his nervous activity, and his faith in the method of treatment.

In this communication we confine ourselves to the statement of general principles concerning methodology in use of hypnotherapy.

Indications toward the use of hypnotherapy in skin diseases may be divided into two large sections; first, broad indications when hypnotherapy is employed merely as an auxiliary method; and second, more specific indications when hypnotherapy is employed as the main and basic technique.

To the section of broad indications belong neurotic conditions in general; insomnia accompanying many dermatoses; various manifestations of nervousness, such as fear of being incurably ill, worry about one's health. All such instances of unbalance of the nerves affect unfavorably the course of the skin ailment. These patients are clearly benefited by hypnosuggestive therapy, but only as an auxiliary method.

When the treatment calls for suggestion or hypnosis as the basic method of treatment, indications are called specific or "limited." Among the dermatoses falling into this category are those already enumerated and many others, for instance, ordinary warts.

It is advisable, for best results, to combine hypnosis with conditioned-reflex action of selected drugs. This is beneficial, even when the patients are highly suggestible, mainly because the therapeutic effect of

176

suggestion does not last long enough. So it occurs that the symptoms of the disease become re-established after a while, sometimes even within several hours. As it is impracticable to employ hypnosis too often, the patient is conditioned to the drug and takes it at intervals between hypnotic sessions. This method assures the continuity of the treatment, and this is particularly advantageous in dealing with chronic illnesses which yield to treatment but slowly. High suggestibility and high conditioning usually go together and thus produce the best results.

In most cases, the formation of a conditioned reflex requires repeated suggestion. If the patient is highly suggestible, it may be done in two or three hypnotic sessions. For this therapy, it is possible to use either medication with definite pharmacological properties (such as luminal for insomnia or dimedrol for itching) and also 'indifferent' drugs. When administered to patients of low suggestibility, the latter may be without effect, for lack of sufficient conditioning.

The conditioned-reflex therapy is particularly useful in the following cases: to eliminate itching and pain, to establish conditioned sleep, to reduce or overcome neurotic symptoms developing in some skin ailments, to counteract various undesirable emotional experiences.

Sessions of hypnosis and conditioned sleep work best when conducted in bed, at the usual sleep time, when the patient may remain hypnotized. Hypnosis gradually passes then into natural sleep.

# HYPNOTHERAPY OF DERMATOSES IN
# RESORT TREATMENT

## by I. A. Zhukov
### (Khosta)

Our study was confined to the role of hypnosuggestive therapy under resort conditions (in Sochi and Matsesta, Caucausus), where dermatoses are extremely common among patients.

The sulphur baths at Matsesta as well as sea and sun bathing constitute the main attractions of the region. The fame, beauty, and excellent climate of this resort environment produce by themselves a favorable influence upon the patients. But the use of psychotherapy on the background of these beneficial factors enables us to attain even quicker and more enduring improvement in the patients' health.

All our hypnotic treatments were conducted by means of the so-called fascination technique (involving staring at some bright object), the spoken word conveying the required suggestion. Evening hours were chosen for the hypnotic sessions, insofar as this time was most compatible with the resort regimen and permitted us to extend the patients' sleep to ten or twelve hours. The sessions were conducted in the patients' own wards.

There were altogether six hundred patients under our observation, suffering from eczema, psoriasis, neuro-dermatitis, and other skin ailments. Of these people three hundred were treated by hypnosis in combination with the usual resort treatment; they constituted the experimental group. The other three hundred people served as the control group and were under resort treatment only.

The patients forming the experimental group had seventeen hypnotic sessions in all.

There were in both groups 270 persons suffering from eczema, half of them under hypnotic treatment and the other half in the control group.

The experimental group was composed of 124 women and eleven men, their age ranging from twenty to sixty-five years. At the time of the treatment, they had suffered from eczema from several months to twenty-five years. Their case histories indicated in all instances some psychological traumata.

Our comparative data, with and without psychotherapy, are most illuminating with regard to percentages of cure and improvement in their illness, as can be easily seen from the following table:

### Table I (ECZEMA)

| Results of Treatment | Control Group | Experimental Group |
|---|---|---|
| Complete Recovery | 13  (9.6%) | 45 (33.3%) |
| Marked Improvement | 16 (11.9%) | 34 (25.2%) |
| Slight Improvement | 83 (61.5%) | 54 (40.0%) |
| No changes | 16 (11.9%) | 2  (1.5%) |
| Deterioration | 7  (5.1%) | —    — |

There were altogether one hundred and sixty-six persons suffering from various forms of neuro-dermatitis, half of them in the experimental group and the other half in the control group.

The comparison of the results achieved in each group is given in the following table:

### Table II (NEURO-DERMATITIS)

| Results of Treatment | Control Group | Experimental Group |
|---|---|---|
| Complete Recovery | 13 (15.7%) | 30 (36.1%) |
| Marked Improvement | 9 (10.8%) | 28 (33.7%) |
| Slight Improvement | 50 (60.2%) | 22 (26.5%) |
| No change | 8 (9.6%) | 3 (3.7%) |
| Deterioration | 3 (3.7%) | — — |

The group suffering from psoriasis consisted of one hundred and forty-four persons, half of them in the experimental group and an equal number in the control group. The patients in the former group were from twenty to sixty years old; the duration of their disease was from one to twenty-five years. In most cases the illness was quite extensive and affected the head, the trunk, and the legs and feet.

The results can be seen in the following table comparing the outcome of treatment in both groups of patients.

### Table III (PSORIASIS)

| Results of Treatment | Control Group | Experimental Group |
|---|---|---|
| Complete Recovery | 3 (4.2%) | 14 (19.5%) |
| Marked Improvement | 12 (16.6%) | 32 (44.4%) |
| Slight Improvement | 48 (66.6%) | 26 (36.1%) |
| No change | 5 (7.0%) | — — |
| Deterioration | 4 (5.6%) | — — |

There was a follow-up of this study of eczema, neuro-dermatitis, and psoriasis. Practically all the patients of the experimental group and many patients of the control group were contacted by means of a questionnaire, and 229 answers were received. The answers overwhelmingly testified to the permanent nature of the improvements.

# PART VI

*GENERAL PROBLEMS*

# PSYCHOTHERAPY OF CONVALESCENCE

## by I. P. Kutanin
### *(Saratov)*

In the light of I. P. Pavlov's findings, every word uttered by a physician plays a significant role in his patient's treatment. The physician must know what he is saying and what effect his words are producing. But it is equally true that the physician should know and understand his patient. And in psychotherapy, the patient must be studied, for he represents a complex and sensitive psychosomatic unity. In the development of various illnesses, the patient's mental state, particularly his emotions, constitute an important ingredient. That is why it is so essential to analyze it.

The main representatives of Russian medical thought—M. Y. Mudrov, G. A. Zakharyin, N. I. Pirogov, N. A. Ostroumov, and others—assigned to the psychogenic factor an important place in the etiology and pathogenesis of disease. V. A. Manasseyin, in commenting upon the role of mental shocks, clearly asserted that "they may not only cause various forms

185

of trouble in the organs of the body, but also disturb general nutrition of the organism."

G. A. Zakharyin often pointed out that "most seriously ill patients, by virtue of their sickness, find themselves in a gloomy mood and look worriedly toward the future. The physician, to be successful in the treatment, must encourage the patient, give him hope of recovery or at least a chance of improvement."

And indeed, many such patients manifest these attitudes according to the degree of their pains, fears, and other negative experiences. In addition to headaches and insomnia, they are likely to have hypochondria, depression, asthenia, apathy, abulia, and other neurotic reactions.

Patients in sanatoriums display capricious behavior, minor deceptions, and lack of discipline. To control this kind of conduct, it is very important to understand the patient's temperament, character, previous illnesses, etc.

Any patient, prior to his arrival to the sanatorium, had probably much to do with other physicians, made inquiries, received much discordant information. The physician at the sanatorium must be aware of all this, make his own diagnosis, and be sure of his findings. This demands of him a great deal of medical knowledge as well as of understanding of human psychology.

Unfortunately, however, it cannot be said that in typical sanatorium practice much attention is being paid to patients' psychological states.

One of the most important tasks for a physician is to calm the patient, to reduce his worries and tensions. Or, to put this differently, among the many functions of psychotherapy is the creation of positive emotions, particularly those connected with optimism, hope and trust. It may be advisable also to consider the psychotherapy of laughter and gay disposition. At the same time we should not forget the occasional value of silence. Both the physicians and nurses should keep in mind that idle, superfluous talk may lead to iatrogeny.

It is necessary to state that treatment by suggestion and hypnosis is not used sufficiently in most sanatoriums. Yet hypnosis definitely represents one of the most effective methods of therapy. It is, to be sure, only one of many forms of psychotherapy and should not be employed indiscriminately or with unjustified optimism. It is to be recommended in the treatment of neuroses (especially their specific symptoms), insomnia, and many other ills. Indirect suggestion may play an important role in connection with prescribed drugs and physiotherapy.

Rational psychotherapy should be widely used, too, particularly in sanatoriums. There should be extensive talks with each patient, mainly in the early days of treatment, so as to comprehend his personality, to clarify the causes of his ailment, and to give him proper explanations and advices. Nor should the physician remain passive with regard to the patient's interpretation of himself and his illness. Any preconception or prejudice should be identified and subjected to suitable but sympathetic criticism.

In addition to rational psychotherapy, a certain amount of educational treatment is often indicated, the purpose of which is to improve the disposition of the patient. Physical culture, permissible sports and games may be quite beneficial in this connection.

Psychotherapy should be interpreted here in its broadest meaning. It may include such activities as: (a) reading of books and magazines; (b) movies from time to time; (c) occasional music; (d) selected physical work; and (e) various cultural activities.

A good book may calm and distract the patient, redirect his thoughts; it may contribute to the reconstruction of his personality. But it may also be harmful. All literature available to patients should be chosen with a clear purpose. Each sanatorium must be equipped with a library designed specially for its kind of patients. Some patients say: "What cured me was books," or "This book is better than any medicine."

Cinema, too, plays a great therapeutic role in resort life. The films shown to the patients should be carefully and wisely selected, for the purpose of treatment rather than for mere entertainment. They should be cheerful and bright in content rather than sad or oppressive; their effect should be to calm and relax.

A certain place must be assigned in therapy also to music, especially among the neurotics. Music makes it possible to alter or raise the patients' mood, or to redirect their thoughts. Everybody knows, in fact, what favorable effect a successful concert or an evening of pleasant activity may have on one's disposition. The positive influence of music had already been observed at the time of V. M. Bekhterev. Our own experience with the psychiatric clinics and observations on the effect of symphonic concerts at Sochi and Kislovodsk confirm the beneficial results of good musical entertainment.

As to the work therapy, long recommended in

psycho-neurotic hospitals, it is advisable only in places where patients remain for a considerable length of time, as in sanatoriums for tubercular cases. But such therapy must be made attractive and as varied as possible. It may be conducted indoors as well as outdoors. Carpentry, work in the garden or kitchen garden, sawing, and painting exemplify the activities that can be organized depending on the kind of patients one deals with and on local opportunities.

It is regrettable that many physicians manifest only a passive attitude toward more cultural activities in the sanatoriums. They usually leave this job to experts in cultural education. Nevertheless, it happens to be very true that games, sports, excursions, literary discussions, and the like establish most favorable conditions for treatment.

The organization of leisure time activities is inseparable from the general regimen of a sanatorium. It should involve the entire staff as well as the patients. The appearance of strict order and punctuality has in such institutions a most desirable effect upon the patients' morale.

The whole atmosphere of the sanatorium must not be dominated, however, by a great variety of activities. It is, above all, a place of rest and peace of mind. The whole staff must see to it that every ward is characterized by the desire to assure the patients' comfort and relaxation.

It is to be expected that in a sanatorium the patients should gain in strength, increase weight, feel better and, in addition, acquire useful habits so essential to their later life and work. Psychohygiene is, after all, a part of general hygiene.

# PSYCHOTHERAPEUTIC FACTORS IN CLINICAL PRACTICE

by A. S. Borzunova, A. V. Sayfutdinova, Z. M.
Akhmetova, O. P. Klimovich, and A. I. Sannikova
*(Ufa and Leningrad)*

This report contains the results of treatment of
293 neurotic patients observed by us during 1950-
1954. We used rational psychotherapy and waking
suggestion, before which each patient and his case
history were carefully studied.

The psychotherapeutic sessions began only with
each patient's approval, after the purpose of the treatment was explained to him. Suggestion was conducted in the following manner. The patient was
taken to a comfortable but somewhat darkened room,
put on a soft couch in a convenient pose, freed from
any tight garments, and asked to close his eyes. Under
these conditions, the nervous system becomes relatively free from strong visual stimuli capable of
diverting his attention or arousing irrelevant thoughts.
Moreover, as long as the patient is relaxed in a lying
position, he does not have to maintain balance,
change his position, make gestures, etc. All this has

a calming effect on the patient, and he becomes quite receptive to the words of the physician saying, for instance, "I shall be speaking plainly and clearly. You will be listening without any effort or tension." This is followed by a therapeutic explanation and suggestion, but no attempt is made to put him to sleep.

Prolonged hypnosis can assume several forms:

1. The physician puts the patient into a hypnotic sleep, with the intention of waking him up after two to four hours.

2. The patient receives the suggestion to sleep until he is awakened by the physician.

3. The patient is told "You will continue sleeping, without any disturbance, and will wake up in four hours."

4. Just about the bed time, the patient receives the following suggestion: "You will be sleeping quite well, without awakening. You will wake up at the usual time in the morning."

In all instances of hypnotic sleep, the patients are under the physician's observation.

In cases of chronic alcoholism, the patients are treated as a group in their own ward while remaining in their beds. Collective hypnosis is used also in cases of hysteria, but only after the patients have been treated individually.

In the following table are shown results of hypnosome collectively. The duration of hypnotic sleep varied from case to case. In seventy-five cases, suggestion was limited to the waking state. Rational psychosis on patients, some put under hypnosis individually, therapy was applied to thirty-nine. In many instances, medication and physiotherapy were combined with hypnosis.

To classify by sex: male patients were 199; female, 94. Out of the total number, sixteen were children. The results of the treatment, classified by disease, were as follows:

| Type of Disease | No. of patients | Cure or Improvement |
|---|---|---|
| Chronic alcoholism | 122 | 74 |
| Neuroses | 105 | 94 |
| Morphinism | 3 | — |
| Hypochondria | 11 | 10 |
| Somatic illness (hypertonia, gastric ulcer, tuberculosis, etc.) | 5 | 5 |
| Cyclothymia | 5 | 5 |
| Reaction-type cases | 36 | 33 |
| Manic-depressive psychosis | 2 | 2 |
| Involuntary melancholia | 1 | — |
| Psychopathic personality | 3 | 1 |

Let us briefly examine a few case histories:

Patient Z. manifested on arrival symptoms of irrepressible vomiting, extreme emaciation, and a paralytic condition of the limbs. Prior to this she had been treated repeatedly; there were indications of internal cancer. In the psychiatric clinic, after a careful examination, the diagnosis was hysteria. Treatment began with rational therapy, was changed to hypnosis and modified to prolonged sleep conducted simultaneously with another patient for ten days. The duration of each session was twenty-two hours per day. At the end of the period there was noticeable improvement. The treatment continued for a while, but soon the patient returned to work.

Patient K., forty-five years of age, was a victim of severe war injuries, with the eventual amputation of the right arm. As a result, there developed phantom sensations including pains in the non-existent fingers of the amputated arm. Several surgical operations were of no avail. A series of hypnotic treatments ended with the elimination of disturbing pains as well as in the restoration of normal attitudes toward his crippled state. Two years later, the symptoms recurred in connection with the death of his son; but several hypnotic sessions sufficed to cure the patient.

Patient X. had suffered from hypochondria for two years. According to him, "he was sick all over, with all internal organs completely inactive." Under the influence of a few sessions of prolonged hypnotic sleep, the patient was able to return to work.

Patient P., a case of pulmonary tuberculosis, was able, when subjected to waking suggestion, to get rid of feelings of discouragement and also to gain weight and overcome asthmatic breathing. In the end, she consented to be transferred to a country institution for the tuberculars.

It is now feasible to conclude that psychotherapy is indicated not only in many cases of neurosis and some cases of psychosis, but also in certain somatic illnesses.

Our experience demonstrates, in general, that psychotherapeutic methods should be used as follows:

1. In persistent neurotic conditions, hypochondria, and psychoses with the hypochondriac syndrome: waking suggestion in a lying position with closed eyes.

2. In somatic ailments: prolonged hypnotic sleep.

3. In hysteria, narcomania, and alcoholism: hypnosis depending on the nature of the case; it may be given different forms, including group hypnosis and prolonged sleep.

4. In depression of various forms: waking suggestion followed by hypnosis.

# PSYCHOTHERAPY IN IATROGENIC ILLNESSES

by M. A. Zhilinskaya and L. G. Pervov
*(Leningrad)*

One of the most important tasks of psychotherapy concerns the question of iatrogenic illnesses. It is regrettable that physicians of various specializations do not take the possibility of iatrogenic influence of their words into serious consideration, especially in the presence of patients with a weakened nervous activity. It is quite natural that many a patient turns to a physician for help precisely during such weakened state and sometimes while afflicted with inhibitions of various degrees and forms. The physician's uncautious word thus becomes an overpowering disturbance. A casual opinion on the part of the physician concerning the nature of the disease or a discussion of the suitable treatment may create in the patient's mind, for instance, an impression either that the disease is extremely grave or that the indicated treatment must be wrong.

An iatrogenic illness may arise when the physician (or a therapist, roentgenologist, surgeon) makes the diagnosis of a somatic disease without adequate grounds, tentatively as it were. Then, in the course of the subsequent treatment, the patient forms certain apparent—not necessarily real—pathological symptoms.

Patient E., for instance, had a serious mental shock: she lost her mother from cancer of the stomach. On the background of a weakened nervous system, she began to complain of stomach pains and visited a physician. The usual many sided investigation of the case only confirmed in the patient the possibility of cancer, the more so that the physician openly considered it. All this does not mean, of course, that various prophylactic steps should not be taken; nevertheless, it is most important to consider the patient's personality, experiences, and the state of her nervous system. Fortunately enough, a rather long psychotherapeutic treatment of the patient was successful in overcoming the phobic syndrome.

It happens also that a patient's physician discusses his case history with somebody else in his presence, without considering the possible impressions. Such situations do commonly occur in the examination of patients or during daily rounds in hospitals or clinics. As a result, the patient may recall the remarks concerning his health or illness and try to comprehend the strange words he heard. The result may be that the existing neurotic condition is unnecessarily aggravated.

Practically all of our patients with iatrogenic symptoms belonged to the weak type of the nervous system. During their examination by means of clinical or physiological methods the same weakness was observed; functions of the autonomic system were considerably modified indicating some disruption of the cortical and subcortical control.

Let us consider a case history.

Patient M., forty years of age. Diagnosis: neurasthenia with a phobic syndrome. His nervous system is of the weak type. Excessive worry of his parents concerning his health since early childhood contributed heavily to the development of the feeling that his health was below par. Every time he met a difficult situation in life he felt sick. The patient entered a hospital complaining of pains in the region of the heart and fear of death. He became particularly sick when a physician, after examining him decided that it might be dangerous for him to go to a resort, insofar as he suffered from hypertonia and myocardiac dystrophy. On his return home, the patient began to feel pains in the heart again. The polyclinic physician ordered him to stay in bed, but another physician making rounds changed the order. The patient was demoralized more than ever. Further examination excluded the possibility of a heart ailment, however, and the patient was transferred to a psychotherapeutic ward. After several psychotherapeutic talks and suggestion, regular walks for exercise, and the use of bromides in small doses (with caffein), the patient gradually recovered. During two years of observation he showed no signs of the former ailment.

Our findings show that the victims of iatrogenic neuroses are mainly persons with nerve weakness. The central task of treatment consists in raising the tonus of the higher nervous system and in removing all noticeable dominant pathological ideas by means of psychotherapy and whatever other means may be available.

The existence of any real trouble, functional or organic, should not be concealed from the patient, under ordinary circumstances. The patient should be informed of the nature of his illness, but, whenever possible, told of its ultimate favorable outcome.

# GROUP PSYCHOTHERAPY AND THE MOVIES

## by L. M. Sukharebsky
### (*Moscow*)

In spite of the considerable experience we have in group psychotherapy, there is no complete unanimity as to the merit of combining the methods of individual and collective treatment. Thus, I. I. Lukomsky does not exactly approve of the use of collective sessions of hypnosis. He is willing to concede that there are some advantages of the method, particularly in the increase of suggestibility and imitativeness, but on the whole he feels convinced that the standard approach to the patient is the only acceptable one in the end.

On the other hand, there are authors who approve of the method of group psychotherapy and who are in favor of combining it, whenever possible, with individual treatment. V. N. Miassischev, for instance, contends that collective psychotherapy provides an important factor in suggestive influence upon the patient, insofar as it greatly enhances its effectiveness. This point of view is shared also by M. S. Lebedinsky who finds that the group method offers some advantages when it is combined with the individual method of treatment.

The available evidence testifies to the effect that each of the methods has its unique features, and sometimes it has to be also combined with other types of therapy, such as medication and physiotherapy. The main thing is to approach each case with proper discrimination.

Half a century of experience with showing motion pictures to all kinds of audiences, including sick people, indicates that films have a many-sided influence upon human psychology. They are, or may be, more than entertainment only. I. S. Sumbayev has demonstrated that, in psychotherapy, words affect people not only as cold meanings, but also as rhythm and tone conveying feelings. He points out that sounds coming from the screen can assume the form of colorful "vocal gestures." They can be pronounced quietly or in whisper; or else they can come to an end in a beautiful and long-remembered song. Sounds can be enhanced by means of accents, pauses, and musical effects of all kinds.

The music of films can be highly beneficial to the patient; it is able to produce a calming effect upon the patient, to provide him with positive emotions. The problem of the value of music in the treatment of patients has been attracting the physicians' attention for a long time. V. M. Bekhterev was active in the field and spoke of the therapeutic results of musical experience.

An interesting and important motion picture, "Once and Forever" was produced a few years ago; it dealt with the treatment of alcoholics by hypnosis. There were three parts to it. The first part had to do with alcoholism as a social evil affecting the family, everyday life, and industry. The content was not merely educational; it also served as a warning or emotional preparation. The second part of the film portrayed a hypnotic session with a medical purpose. The public saw a group of individuals on the screen, all suffering from alcoholism in various stages and forms; they also had an opportunity to see Professor Y. V. Kannabih putting the patients to sleep. The third part constituted an attempt to hypnotize the living audience. It aimed at mass hypnosis conducted directly from the screen. All the stages of psychotherapeutic influence were organically brought together thus increasing the influence of suggestion. Examination of the results showed a high psychotherapeutic effectiveness of the picture.

Unfortunately, the number of films of this caliber is still comparatively small. But for the purposes of psychoprophylaxis even ordinary films of high quality may be very useful. And indeed, observations in the First Moscow Medical Institute have demonstrated that certain films have a considerable psychotherapeutic effect.

It has been frequently observed that when patients obsessed by unhappy memories or thoughts have an opportunity to see a gay and stimulating motion picture, they seem to leave the habitual mental states behind, at least for a while.

Excellent influence upon patients was actually produced by such musical comedy films as "Anton Ivanovich is Angry" or "Air Coachman." When adapted for demonstration in ordinary wards, they offered a valuable form of relaxation.

Some high quality films are definitely recommended for audiences of sick children. Demonstration of a picture like "Doctor Ouch" does much good to such children. It is well known that our youngsters are sometimes afraid of the physicians, resist medical examination, interfere with temperature taking, and refuse to swallow medicine. But the films like "Doctor Ouch" or "Limpopo" quite often change the children's attitude toward medical procedures, drugs, and physicians.

We have actually seen that when a worried child is reminded of the good Doctor Ouch, he often consents to take medicine or have his temperature measured. The role of films as a psychotherapeutic factor must not be underestimated.

In all psychoneurological centers, high quality films are now shown regularly and as a matter of course. But the responsibility for the job is often left in the hands of the entertainment staff, while the physicians keep their hands off and are not even consulted.

Yet, whenever films of emotional intensity and struggle are shown to the patients, the results may consist in the deterioration of their health. Some of them, after watching a motion picture of this sort, have difficulty in falling asleep. It follows that the choice of films for sick people must be made more cautiously, preferably after consultation with a physician.

It is desirable, furthermore, that the demonstration of films be preceded by a physician's address to the patients (no longer than ten or fifteen minutes), in which they are informed concerning the content and type of the film. The purpose of the talk is, of course, psychotherapeutic. In some cases, the showing of the motion picture may be also followed by a talk or discussion.

# INDEX

## A

Abstract thinking, 4
Agalactia, 169, 171
*Akhmetova, Z. M.,* 190-194
Alcoholism, 129-143
Anamnesis, 11, 70
*Andres,* 161
*Andreyev, A. M.,* 79
*Androsova, Z. G.,* 52
Anesthesia, 28, 78-83
Apomorphine, 131, 134, 136-140
*Apter, I. M.,* 89-93
*Aryev, M. Y.,* 155
Astasia-abasia, 88
Asthma, bronchial, 155-160
Attitudes, 7, 70
Autonomic nervous system, 22
Auto-suggestion, 62, 86-87

## B

*Barker,* 45
Basedow's disease, 33, 161-164

*Bekhterev, V. M.,* 18, 36, 61, 72, 80, 87, 131, 188, 200
*Belous, V. M.,* 156
*Belyaeva, A. T.,* 169-170
*Bergwin,* 45
*Bernheim, H.,* 61, 80
*Bernstein, A. N.,* 156
Bio-electrical activity, 44-51
*Birman, B. N.,* 73
*Blake,* 45
*Bobkov, V. V.,* 45
*Bonhafer, K.,* 129
*Botkin, S. P.,* 155, 161
*Borzunova, A. S.,* 190-194
*Bowles,* 45
*Bull, I. I.,* 155-159
*Bykov, K. M.,* 22, 118, 164

## C

*Chernorutzky, M. V.,* 155
Child psychiatry, 94-97
*Chistovich, A. S.,* 80
*Chitava, O. R.,* 82-84
Circumstantial reflex, 123

Clinics, 3, 190-194
*Colier, O. R.*, 119
Compulsion, 83
Conditioned reflexes, 41-43
Conditioned-reflex therapy 172-177
Convalescence, 185-189
*Crendley*, 46

### D

*Danilov, I. V.*, 52
*Dennes*, 45
Dermatoses, 172-181
*Dezherin*, 26
Digestive secretion, 52-54
Distraction, 17-18
*Dombrovskaya, U. F.*, 169
*Dondysh, L. M.*, 135
*Draznin, N. M.*, 162
*Dubois*, 161

### E

Eczema, 179
Emotions, 7, 23
Encephalography, 44-50
Epilepsy, 32
Euphoria, 88
Extended sleep, 83-84, 122-125

### F

Feeding, suggested, 53-54
*Forbes*, 45
*Ford*, 45
*Forel, A.*, 61
*Frank*, 45, 46
*Freud, S.*, 19, 39

Frigidity, 16-17
*Frolov, Y. P.*, 155
*Fuchs, V. G.*, 52

### G

*Gannushkin, P. B.*, 72
*Gerard*, 46
*Gershuni, G. V.*, 79
*Goldberg, E. I.*, 135
*Golubov, N. F.*, 155
*Gordova, T. N.*, 136-140
Group therapy, 19, 57-60
*Guiliarovsky, V. A.*, 79, 97, 98, 100

### H

*Haletsky, A. M.*, 73-77
Hallucination, 106-107
*Harvey*, 45
*Hobart*, 45
*Hornborng*, 52
Hypnosis, 13, 22, 30-31, 40-51, 55-56, 106-107, 122-123, 131-133, 136-143, 146, 152, 156, 158-160, 163-164, 168, 172-181, 187, 191-194
Hypnotarium, 137
Hypochondriasis, 83, 119, 193
Hypogalactia, 169-171
Hysteria, 14-16, 31-32, 40-43, 78-81, 83-88
Hysterical paralysis, 88

### I

Iatrogeny, 195-198
Impotence, psychogenic, 89-93

204

Indirect suggestion, 85-88
Inger, 45
Inhibition, 40, 56-57
Ivanov, N. V., 57-60
Ivanov-Smolensky, A. G., 24, 73, 82, 150

### K

Kannabih, Y. V., 201
Kantorovich, N. V., 105-112
Kashpur, M. I., 33, 161-164
Kirzon, M. V., 119
Klimovich, O. P., 190-194
Konstorum, S. I., 114
Koopman, 45
Kopelovich, M. A., 162
Kopil-Levina, Z. A., 78-81
Korotkin, I. I., 40-43
Korsakov, S. S., 36, 129
Kovalev, N. K., 136-140
Kozlov, Y. G., 119
Kraepelin, E., 129
Kravchenko, T. M., 169-170
Kurtsin, I. T., 118
Kutanin, I. P., 185-189
Kuymova, N. I., 169-170

### L

Lachman, D. M., 151
Lebedinsky, M. S., 37-39, 199
Lenin, V. I., 6
Leucocytes, 56
Levin, Y. M., 52-54
Liebault, A. A., 61
Liechtenstein, L. I., 122-125
Loewenbach, 45

Loomis, 45
Lukomsky, I. L., 129-135, 199
Lundholm, 45

### M

Makarenko, A. S., 7
Malkova, M. P., 56
Manasseyin, V. A., 185
Marenina, A. I., 44, 45
Marinesco, 46
Marx, A., 156
Marx, K., 6
Maslov, M. S., 169, 170
Masturbation, 90-91
Maximova, T. P., 52
Medical ethics, 88
Medication, 117-118, 132, 145-146, 173
Medicinal sleep, 82-84
Miassischev, V. N., 3-20, 69, 70, 97, 199
Miloslavsky, M. Y., 33
Molokhov, A. N., 113-116
Movies, 188, 199-202
Mudrov, M. Y., 185
Music, 188
Mutism, 79-80

### N

Narbutovich, I. O., 141-143
Natochin, Y. V., 52
Neurasthenia, 14
Neuro-dermitis, 180
Neuroses, 3, 57-60, 69-101, 174, 176, 193
Nevsky, M. P., 44-51

## O

Obsession, 14
Obstetrics, 33-34, 165-167
*Ostroumov, N. A.*, 185

## P

Painless birth, 165-168
*Panurova, V. N.*, 52
*Pavlov, B. V.*, 45
*Pavlov, I. P.*, 4-6, 9, 13, 30,
  24, 53, 69, 72, 73, 82,
  95, 114, 141, 155, 156, 164,
  185
Personality, 6-7
Persuasion, 12-13, 25,
  106-108, 110-111, 146-147
*Pervov, L. G.*, 195-198
*Petrova, M. K.*, 73
Phobia, 32, 73-77, 83
Physiology, 6
*Pirogov, N. I.*, 185
*Platonov, K. I.*, 21-36, 72, 82
*Polyak-Braginskaya, I. Y.*, 169
*Popov, E. A.*, 70, 73
*Povorinsky, Y. A.*, 45, 130,
  132, 144-152
*Poznansky, A. S.*, 117-121
*Proniayeva, K. V.*, 34
Psoriasis, 179-180
Psychasthenia, 69-72, 83
Psychiatry, 5
Psychology, 4-5, 114
Psychoses, 105-125

## R

*Rapoport, A. M.*, 15
Rapport, selective, 141-143

Re-education, 72, 97
*Rodossky, A.*, 155
*Rozhnov, V. E.*, 136, 141, 156
*Rybakov, F. E.*, 129
*Rybushkin, I. N.*, 52

## S

*Sager*, 46
Sanatoriums, 186-189
*Sannikova, A. I.*, 190-194
*Sayfutdinova, A. V.*, 190-194
Schizophrenia, 109-110, 125
*Schreiber, Y. L.*, 85-88
*Sechenov, I. M.*, 155
Secondary signal system, 6,
  21, 82
Self-education, 72
*Serov, S. I.*, 55
*Sheftel, I. N.*, 52
*Shershevskaya, O. I.*, 80
*Shminke, G. A.*, 55
*Simpson, T. N.*, 197
*Singaylo, A. K.*, 56
*Sirna*, 45
Sleep, 96
Smoking, 144-152
Speech, 4, 6
Speech therapy, 12, 21-35, 82
*Spielberg, P. I.*, 44, 45
*Stanislavsky, K. S.*, 74
*Stoyko, A. G.*, 151
*Strielchuk, I. V.*, 130, 135,
  136, 144, 145, 151
Stuttering, 98-101
*Subbotnik, S. N.*, 44
Suggestion, 26, 28-29, 124, 187
*Sukharebsky, L. M.*, 199-202
*Sukharev, G. E.*, 97

206

*Sumbayev, I. S.,* 61-65, 200
*Suslova, M. M.,* 40-43

## T

*Tatarenko, N. P.,* 73, 130
*Thompson,* 45
Thyreotoxicosis,
  psychogenic, 161-164
*Tokareva, I. G.,* 117-121
*Tokarevsky, A. A.,* 61
*Train,* 46
Traumatic psychosis, 108-109
*Troshin, A. K.,* 55-56
*Tsvetkov, I. T.,* 34

## U

*Ukhtomsky, A. A.,* 155
Unconditioned reflex, 7

## V

*Vassilyev, L. L.,* 155
*Veshapelli, N. G.,* 94-97
*Vigdorovich, D. A.,* 156
*Vilkomirsky,* 161
*Vinokurov, G. I.,* 169-170
*Vishnevsky, A. A.,* 119

*Vlassova, N. A.,* 98-101
*Vvedensky, N. E.,* 155

## W

Waking suggestion, 61-65,
  90, 106
*Wetterstrand, O.,* 156
Words, 22
Work, 124-125
Work therapy, 188-189

## Y

*Yakovleva, E. K.,* 15, 69-72
*Yudin, S. S.,* 52, 53, 54

## Z

*Zakharyin, G. A.,* 185-186
*Zdravomyslov, V. I.,* 34, 53,
  165-167, 169-170
*Zeitlin, M. I.,* 117-121
*Zheltakov, M. M.,* 172-177
*Zhlinskaya, M. A.,* 195-198
*Zhislin, S. G.,* 130
*Zhukov, I. A.,* 34, 178-181
*Zuckerman, A. M.,* 119
*Zurabashvili, A. D.,* 82